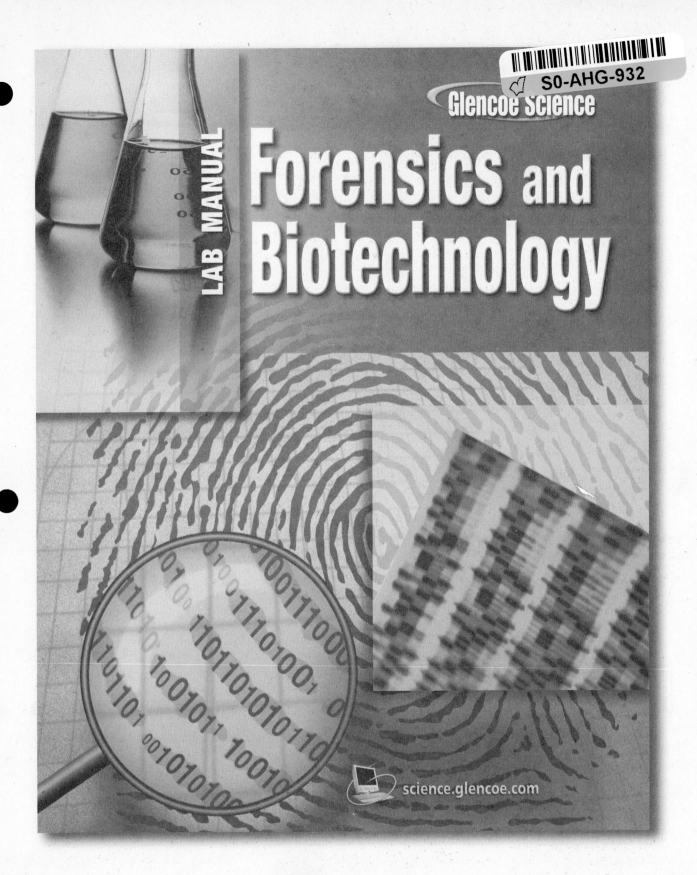

SO-AHG-932

Glencoe Science

LAB MANUAL

Forensics and Biotechnology

science.glencoe.com

Glencoe

New York, New York   Columbus, Ohio   Chicago, Illinois   Peoria, Illinois   Woodland Hills, California

Glencoe

The *McGraw·Hill* Companies

Send all inquiries to:
Glencoe/McGraw-Hill
8787 Orion Place
Columbus, OH 43240-4027

ISBN 0-07-860223-8

Printed in the United States of America.

3 4 5 6 7 8 9 10   009   08 07 06 05

Contents

To the Teacher

Glencoe's Forensics and Biotechnology Lab Manual features ten investigations that use biotechnology techniques to solve real-world problems. This series of investigative hands-on labs is easily integrated into your curriculum. Lab activities emphasize the use of scientific inquiry as a way of thinking and problem solving while relating scientific processes to technological and societal issues.

Students often benefit from a relevant frame of reference for learning abstract concepts. The goal of these labs is to involve students, usually working cooperatively, in extended, in-depth science experiences investigating DNA, collecting and analyzing data, or interpreting evidence found at a crime or accident scene.

Each lab begins with *The Problem*, which describes either a biotechnology issue or the discovery of a crime or accident. Information is presented in *Background* to guide students' understanding of the nature of science by collecting and analyzing data to solve a problem. In *Procedure*, students are given suggestions for completing the lab using steps that teach science process skills, such as observing and inferring. While participating in these labs, students will be confronted with topics such as inheritance and genetically related diseases, pathology, and blood types. The lab's final section, *Analyze and Conclude*, emphasizes the importance of accurate recording and interpretation of data.

In the *Teacher Guide*, you will find the answer guide along with lab materials and supply lists, teaching strategies, expected outcomes, suggestions for time management, and tips for managing classroom activities.

Correlation to Glencoe Biology Programs

The activities in *Glencoe's Forensics and Biotechnology Lab Manual* coordinate with the following chapters/units in these Glencoe biology programs. Use this chart to help plan the best way to use these activities with your class.

	Biology: The Dynamics of Life	Biology: An Everyday Experience	BSCS Biology: A Molecular Approach	Biology: Living Systems	Biology: A Community Context
Lab 1: Where did they drown?	Chapter 8	Chapter 2	Chapter 3	Chapter 4	Chapter 4
Lab 2: How can you extract DNA from cells?	Chapter 13	Chapter 28	Chapter 15	Chapter 10	Chapter 5
Lab 3: How can you transform cells with DNA?	Chapter 13	Chapter 28	Chapter 15	Chapter 10	Chapter 5
Lab 4: How can you transcribe and translate genes?	Chapter 13	Chapter 28	Chapter 15	Chapter 10	Chapter 5
Lab 5: How can you diagnose geneotypes using DNA?	Chapter 13	Chapter 28	Chapter 15	Chapter 10	Chapter 5
Lab 6: How can genetically engineered plants be multiplied?	Chapters 13, 24	Chapters 23, 28	Chapters 12, 15	Chapters 9, 10, 18	Chapter 5
Lab 7: When did she die?	Chapters 34, 35	Chapter 10	Chapters 2, 7	Chapters 20, 26	Chapter 4
Lab 8: A Sweet Season	Chapter 35	Chapter 15	Chapter 9	Chapter 24	Chapter 4
Lab 9: Use Blood Types to Help Solve a Crime	Chapter 12	Chapter 12	Chapter 13	Chapter 21	Chapter 5
Lab 10: The Missing Restaurant Owner	Chapters 12, 13	Chapters 12, 28	Chapters 13, 15	Chapters 10, 21	Chapter 5

Safety and Disposal of Lab Materials

Teaching science requires the use of certain supplies and safety equipment to maintain a safe classroom. The activities in *Glencoe's Forensics and Biotechnology Lab Manual* minimize dangers in the laboratory. Even so, there are no guarantees against accidents. For additional help, refer to the booklet *Glencoe Laboratory Management and Safety in the Science Classroom,* which contains safety guidelines and masters to test students' lab and safety skills.

General Guidelines

- Post safety guidelines, fire escape routes, and a list of emergency procedures in the classroom. Make sure students understand these procedures. Remind them at the beginning of *every* lab session.
- Understand and make note of the safety symbols used in the activities.
- Have students fill out a safety contract. Students should pledge to follow the rules, to wear safety attire, and to conduct themselves in a responsible manner.
- Know where emergency equipment is stored and how to use it.
- Perform all activities before you allow students to do so.
- Supervise students at all times. Check assembly of all setups.
- Instruct students to follow directions carefully and to not take shortcuts or switch steps.
- Make sure that all students are wearing proper safety attire. Do not permit wearing contact lenses, even with safety glasses; splashing chemicals could infuse under a lens and cause eye damage.

Handling Electronic Equipment

- Instruct students on the safety guidelines provided by the manufacturer of your calculator(s) and probe(s).
- Check wiring for damage before each use. Do not use if frayed.
- Do not use the equipment where it could get wet.
- Do not allow students to eat or drink while using the equipment.
- Unplug the calculator when not in use.

- Caution students to use care when handling the equipment. Calculators and probes should not be shaken or dropped.
- Store the equipment properly when not in use.

Handling Chemicals

- Always wear safety goggles, gloves, and an apron when handling chemicals. Treat all chemicals as potentially dangerous.
- Never ingest chemicals. Use proper techniques to smell solutions.
- Use a fume hood when handling chemicals that are poisonous or corrosive or that give off a vapor.
- Know the location of an eyewash station. Flush the eyewash for five minutes once a week to remove harmful contaminants that may grow in the eyewash. Do not use a squeeze bottle as a substitute for an eyewash.
- Always add acids to water, never the reverse.
- Prepare solutions by adding the solid to a small amount of distilled water and then diluting with water to the volume listed. If you use a hydrate that is different from the one specified in a particular preparation, you will need to adjust the amount of hydrate to obtain the correct concentration.
- Consider purchasing premixed solutions from a scientific supply house to reduce the amount of chemicals on hand.
- Maintain appropriate MSDS (Materials Safety Data Sheets) in the laboratory.

Chemical Storage

- Use wood shelving, rather than metal, that is firmly attached to the wall.
- Equip shelves with a lip to prevent chemicals from being jarred off the shelf.

- Store only those chemicals you intend to use.
- Store chemicals in upright positions no more than three containers deep.
- Store chemicals at or below eye level but not on the floor.
- Make sure all containers are labeled to identify the contents, concentration, date purchased or prepared, safety precautions for handling, expiration date, and manufacturer's name and address.
- Separate chemicals by reaction type. For example, store acids in one place and bases in another. Store oxidants away from easily oxidized materials.
- Store flammables in an approved flammable cabinet.

Chemical Disposal

- Maintain an ongoing chemical inventory. Remove chemicals that are out-of-date, contaminated, or lacking legible labels.
- Consult local and state authorities for disposal methods. Use a reference such as *Prudent Practices in the Laboratory: Handling and Disposal of Chemicals* (National Academy Press, 1995) for general guidelines on handling and disposing of chemicals. Current laws in your area supersede the information in this book.
- Neutralize any substance that has a pH less than 3 or greater than 8 before disposal.

- For substances that can be flushed down a drain, flush with at least 100 times its volume of tap water.
- Consider utilizing a commercial chemical disposal company.

Chemical Spills

- Maintain a clearly identified spill kit in the science lab that contains commercial materials for that purpose. You also can keep a container of dry sand or dry clay available; remember that these will not neutralize an acid or base.
- Contain the spill and neutralize the chemical if necessary.
- Remove the material with equipment made of plastic or polypropylene to prevent reaction with any chemical that remains.
- Place the material in plastic bags or containers and label appropriately.
- Inform the custodial staff of proper disposal of the material.
- For a major spill, such as breaking a liter bottle of hydrochloric acid, take the following actions:
  ➤ Evacuate all students through the exits farthest from the spill.
  ➤ Assist any person splashed with the chemical to the safety shower.
  ➤ Contain the spill wearing proper protective clothing. Do not allow the spill to trap you.
  ➤ Call for help.

DISCLAIMER

Glencoe/McGraw-Hill makes no claims to the completeness of this discussion of laboratory safety and chemical storage. The information presented is not all-inclusive, nor does it address all of the hazards associated with the handling, storage, and disposal of chemicals, or with laboratory practices and management.

Forensics and Biotechnology Materials Supply List

Labs	Everyday Materials	Lab Materials
Lab 1 **Where did they drown?**	tissues marker string (optional)	distilled water 25-mL graduated cylinder 250-mL graduated cylinder 250-mL beakers (7) balance that is sensitive to at least 0.1 g 2.5 cm $\times$ 30 cm pieces of water-soaked dialysis tubing (7) sucrose solutions (1%, 5%, 10%, 20%, 40%)
Lab 2 **How can you extract DNA from cells?**	blender banana 5-oz plastic cups (2) color-free shampoo table salt plastic spoon #2 cone coffee filter	pipette or dropper 270 mL distilled water sealed (rubber stopper) test tube containing cold alcohol (95% ethanol or 91% isopropyl)
Lab 3 **How can you transform cell with new DNA?**	plastic container of ice marking pen straws (2)	micropipette (2) incubator 100-μL aliquots Luria broth (2) 10-μL aliquot plasmid DNA (1) 100-μL aliquots competent *E.coli* cells (2) plates of culture medium with ampicillin
Lab 4 **How can you transcribe and translate genes?**	paper pencil	your Biology textbook
Lab 5 **How can you diagnose genotypes using DNA?**	clear glass plate	test tubes containing simulated DNA fragments (7) gel cassette for electrophoresis P-20 micro-pipette with seven tips 150-mL 1X TAE buffer gel electrophoresis box
Lab 6 **How can genetically engineered plants be multiplied?**	bleach detergent razor blade marking pen sugar scissors African violet leaves (2) prepackaged African violet medium	sterile Petri dishes (5) agar Powder latex gloves distilled water 1 L sterile water 250-mL beaker stirring rod pH meter or paper dropper 250-mL bottle sterile forceps parafilm 250-mL or larger glass jar with screw-cap lid NaOH and HCl (as needed to adjust pH) 70% ethanol in a spray bottle
Lab 7 **When did she die?**	calculator graph paper ruler	your Biology textbook
Lab 8 **A Sweet Season**	tissues ruler graph paper watch with a second hand display or stopwatch	labeled test tubes (12) glucose test strips (12) copy of test strip color chart
Lab 9 **Use Blood Types to Help Solve a Crime**	bleach paper towels	ABO/Rh blood-typing test kit (with artificial or aseptic blood samples)
Lab 10 **The Missing Restaurant Owner**	paper pencil	your Biology textbook

Suppliers

American Science & Surplus
P.O. Box 1030
Skokie, IL 60076
1-847-647-0011
www.sciplus.com

Bio-Rad Laboratories
2000 Alfred Nobel Dr.
Life Science Group
Hercules, CA 94547
(800) 876-3425
www.biorad.com

Carolina Biological Supply Co.
2700 York Road
Burlington, NC 27215
(800) 334-5551
carolina.com

Edmund Scientifics
60 Pearce Ave.
Tonawanda, NY 14150-6711
(800) 728-6999
www.scientificsonline.com

Fisher Science Education
4500 Turnberry
Hanover Park, IL 60133
(800) 955-1177
fisheredu.com

Nasco Science
901 Janesville Avenue
P.O. Box 901
Fort Atkinson, WI 53538-0901
(800) 558-9595
www.nascofa.com

Nebraska Scientific
3823 Leavenworth St.
Omaha, NE 68105-1180
(800) 228-7117
nebraskascientific.com

PASCO Scientific
10101 Foothills Blvd.
Roseville, CA 95747-7100
(800) 772-8700
pasco.com

Sargent-Welch/VWR Scientific Products
P.O. Box 5229
Buffalo Grove, IL 60089-5229
(800) SAR-GENT
www.sargentwelch.com

Ward's Natural Science Est.
5100 W. Henrietta Road
P.O. Box 92912
Rochester, NY 14692-9012
(800) 962-2660
www.wardsci.com

Contents

To the Student

In the real world, biology is often used to solve problems—sometimes even to solve mysteries. Biologists may examine problems in order to improve human life, such as: "How can a rice crop be made more disease resistant?" and "How can a genetic disease in humans be detected?" Biology can also be used to solve mysteries by answering questions like: "When and how did a person die?" and "To whom does the blood or other biological evidence at a crime scene belong?" Biologists work in the fields of forensics and biotechnology to find the answers to these and many other questions.

In *Glencoe's Forensics and Biotechnology Lab Manual,* you will be presented with in-depth investigations that deal with DNA, collecting and analyzing data, or interpreting evidence found at a crime or accident scene. You will use your knowledge of scientific inquiry and your problem-solving skills as you learn current biotechnology techniques and forensics procedures. You will then apply these techniques and procedures to real-world scenarios.

Each lab begins with *The Problem,* a section that describes either a biotechnology issue or the discovery of a crime or accident. Information in the *Background* section will help you understand the science involved in the problem or case. The *Procedure* section provides step-by-step instructions for learning a technique or procedure or for solving the problem presented. Finally, the *Analyze and Conclude* section allows you to interpret your data and demonstrate your problem-solving skills and understanding of the scientific processes involved.

FORENSICS AND BIOTECHNOLOGY

Laboratory and Safety Guidelines

Emergencies

- Inform the teacher immediately of *any* mishap—fire, injury, glassware breakage, chemical spills, and so forth.
- Know the location of the fire extinguisher, safety shower, eyewash, fire blanket, and first-aid kit. Know how to use this equipment.
- If chemicals come into contact with your eyes or skin, flush with large quantities of water and notify your teacher immediately.

Preventing Accidents

- Do NOT wear clothing that is loose enough to catch on anything. Do NOT wear sandals or open-toed shoes. Remove loose jewelry—chains or bracelets—while doing lab work.
- Wear protective safety gloves, goggles, and aprons as instructed.
- Always wear safety goggles (not glasses) in the laboratory.
- Wear goggles throughout the entire activity, cleanup, and handwashing.
- Keep your hands away from your face while working in the laboratory.
- Remove synthetic fingernails before working in the lab (these are highly flammable).
- Do NOT use hair spray, mousse, or other flammable hair products just before or during laboratory work where an open flame is used (they can ignite easily).
- Tie back long hair and loose clothing to keep them away from flames and equipment.
- Eating, drinking, chewing gum, applying makeup, and smoking are prohibited in the laboratory.
- Do NOT inhale vapors or taste, touch, or smell any chemical or substance unless instructed to do so by your teacher.

Working in the Laboratory

- Study all instructions before you begin a laboratory or field activity. Ask questions if you do not understand any part of the activity.
- Work ONLY on activities assigned by your teacher. NEVER work alone in the laboratory.
- Do NOT substitute other chemicals/substances for those listed in your activity.
- Do NOT begin any activity until directed to do so by your teacher.
- Do NOT handle any equipment without specific permission.
- Remain in your own work area unless given permission by your teacher to leave it.
- Do NOT point heated containers—test tubes, flasks, and so forth—at yourself or anyone else.
- Do NOT take any materials or chemicals out of the classroom.
- Stay out of storage areas unless you are instructed to be there and are supervised by your teacher.

Laboratory Cleanup

- Keep work, lab, and balance areas clean, limiting the amount of easily ignitable materials.
- Turn off all burners, water faucets, probeware, and calculators before leaving the lab.
- Carefully dispose of waste materials as instructed by your teacher.
- With your goggles on, wash your hands thoroughly with soap and warm water after each activity.

Safety Symbols

SAFETY SYMBOLS	HAZARD	EXAMPLES	PRECAUTION	REMEDY
DISPOSAL	Special disposal procedures need to be followed.	certain chemicals, living organisms	Do not dispose of these materials in the sink or trash can.	Dispose of wastes as directed by your teacher.
BIOLOGICAL	Organisms or other biological materials that might be harmful to humans	bacteria, fungi, blood, unpreserved tissues, plant materials	Avoid skin contact with these materials. Wear mask or gloves.	Notify your teacher if you suspect contact with material. Wash hands thoroughly.
EXTREME TEMPERATURE	Objects that can burn skin by being too cold or too hot	boiling liquids, hot plates, dry ice, liquid nitrogen	Use proper protection when handling.	Go to your teacher for first aid.
SHARP OBJECT	Use of tools or glassware that can easily puncture or slice skin	razor blades, pins, scalpels, pointed tools, dissecting probes, broken glass	Practice common-sense behavior and follow guidelines for use of the tool.	Go to your teacher for first aid.
FUME	Possible danger to respiratory tract from fumes	ammonia, acetone, nail polish remover, heated sulfur, moth balls	Make sure there is good ventilation. Never smell fumes directly. Wear a mask.	Leave foul area and notify your teacher immediately.
ELECTRICAL	Possible danger from electrical shock or burn	improper grounding, liquid spills, short circuits, exposed wires	Double-check setup with teacher. Check condition of wires and apparatus.	Do not attempt to fix electrical problems. Notify your teacher immediately.
IRRITANT	Substances that can irritate the skin or mucous membranes of the respiratory tract	pollen, moth balls, steel wool, fiberglass, potassium permanganate	Wear dust mask and gloves. Practice extra care when handling these materials.	Go to your teacher for first aid.
CHEMICAL	Chemicals that can react with and destroy tissue and other materials	bleaches such as hydrogen peroxide; acids such as sulfuric acid, hydrochloric acid; bases such as ammonia, sodium hydroxide	Wear goggles, gloves, and an apron.	Immediately flush the affected area with water and notify your teacher.
TOXIC	Substance may be poisonous if touched, inhaled, or swallowed.	mercury, many metal compounds, iodine, poinsettia plant parts	Follow your teacher's instructions.	Always wash hands thoroughly after use. Go to your teacher for first aid.
OPEN FLAME	Open flame may ignite flammable chemicals, loose clothing, or hair.	alcohol, kerosene, potassium permanganate, hair, clothing	Tie back hair. Avoid wearing loose clothing. Avoid open flames when using flammable chemicals. Be aware of locations of fire safety equipment.	Notify your teacher immediately. Use fire safety equipment if applicable.

Eye Safety
Proper eye protection should be worn at all times by anyone performing or observing science activities.

Clothing Protection
This symbol appears when substances could stain or burn clothing.

Animal Safety
This symbol appears when safety of animals and students must be ensured.

Radioactivity
This symbol appears when radioactive materials are used.

Lab 1 Where did they drown?

The Problem

The Coast Guard discovered two bodies, a man and a woman, in the salt water of the San Francisco Bay. Both victims apparently drowned; their lungs were filled with water, and a frothy mixture of water, air, and mucus was found in their mouths and airways. Your job as the coroner will be to determine where the victims drowned and whether the victims died of accidental drowning or were victims of murder. To help you in your determination, you have taken blood samples from both victims. You must interpret the findings from these blood samples to solve the mystery.

Background

Our bodies contain many compartments of liquid water, such as blood, tissues, and fluids between tissues. This water is composed of many substances, including salts, sugars, and proteins which have dissolved in the water. The concentration of any given substance is the amount of that substance per unit volume of water. Cells, such as those found in the walls of blood vessels and tissues, separate the various compartments of water. The membranes of these cells control which molecules can move between the compartments by allowing some molecules to pass through while limiting others. This is known as selective permeability.

Diffusion How do you know which way substances will move through a membrane? Generally, substances move from an area of high concentration to an area of low concentration. This movement is called diffusion. Diffusion occurs in solids, liquids, and gases. For example, if you cut an onion at the back of your classroom, people at the front of the room will eventually be able to smell it because molecules from the onion are transmitted (diffused) from an area of high concentration (the back of the room) to an area of low concentration (the front of the room). Diffusion continues until the concentration of molecules from the onion in the air is equal in all areas of the room.

All substances, including water, can diffuse. However, the diffusion of water across a selectively permeable membrane has a different name, *osmosis*. Suppose you have two solutions of sugar of different concentrations (high and low) in a clear box. A membrane that is permeable to water but not to sugar separates the two solutions. High concentration is on the left side, and low concentration is on the right side, as shown in Part A of **Figure 1**. The solution on the left has a higher sugar concentration relative to the one on the right and is said to be *hypertonic* to the one on the right. The solution on the right has a lower sugar concentration compared to the one on the left and is said to be *hypotonic* to the solution on the left.

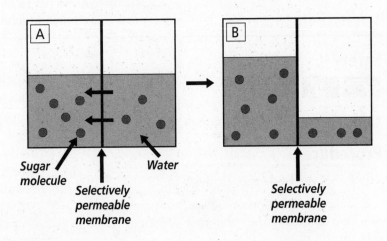

Figure 1

FORENSICS AND BIOTECHNOLOGY

Lab 1
Where did they drown? *continued*

The more sugar that is dissolved in water, the less concentrated the water becomes; in other words, pure water is 100% water, and the concentration of water decreases as you add sugar. Therefore, the concentration of water on the left side is less than that on the right side. As a result, water will diffuse from the right to the left until the concentrations of water on both sides of the membrane are equal, as shown in Part B of **Figure 1**. At that time, the concentrations of sugar on both sides of the membrane will also be equal, or *isotonic*. Solutions in your body behave the same way.

Diffusion in the Lungs Your lungs form a compartment of air separated from a compartment of water (your blood) by cells that make up the air sacs called alveoli. When you breathe, gases diffuse from one compartment to another. Oxygen diffuses from the air into the blood, and carbon dioxide from the blood diffuses into the air. When a person drowns, the lungs fill with freshwater or salt water, depending on the type of water in which he or she

drowned. The blood and lungs become two water-filled compartments (similar to **Figure 1**) in which water can move across the membranes separating the blood and the lungs. Salts in the compartments do not move across the membranes.

In this lab, you will simulate what happens in the human body when a person drowns. You will use sugar solutions to represent the solutions of water, salt, and other substances found in the lungs and blood. Solutions in beakers represent the blood; dialysis tubes, which are selectively permeable membranes, represent the alveoli of the lungs; and solutions in the dialysis tubes represent water in the lungs. You will first experiment with several beakers and dialysis tubes containing different concentrations of sugar representing hypertonic, hypotonic, and isotonic solutions. These will help you understand the movement of water that occurs with the differing solutions. Finally, two solution combinations will represent what happens when a person drowns in freshwater and in salt water.

Everyday Materials
- ❏ string (optional)
- ❏ tissues
- ❏ marker

Lab Materials
- ❏ sucrose solutions (1%, 5%, 10%, 20%, 40%)
- ❏ 250-mL beakers (7)
- ❏ 2.5 cm × 30 cm pieces of water-soaked dialysis tubing (7)

- ❏ distilled water
- ❏ 250-mL graduated cylinder
- ❏ 25-mL graduated cylinder
- ❏ balance that is sensitive to at least 0.1 g

Safety

- Never eat or drink anything in the lab.

Procedure

1. Label the beakers A through G.

2. Take each section of dialysis tubing and tie one end using the tube itself or string. Be careful not to tear the bag.

3. Fill each dialysis tube with 25 mL of sucrose solution, according to the table on the next

page. The tubes should be about $\frac{1}{3}$ full. Fill each beaker with 150 mL of sucrose solution according to the table.

4. Once you fill a dialysis bag, squeeze the air out and tie the remaining end a few centimeters above the top of the liquid without tearing the bag. Rinse the bag with distilled water, blot it dry with a tissue, and weigh it on the balance. Record the mass in the table on the next page (initial bag mass) and place the bag in the appropriate beaker. Repeat this procedure for each bag.

5. Allow each bag to stay in the beaker for 30 minutes.

Lab

1   Where did they drown? *continued*

6. After 30 minutes, remove each bag, rinse with distilled water, blot dry, and determine its mass. Record the mass in the table (final bag mass). Measure the amount of liquid that remains in the beaker after the bag is removed. Discard the bags and empty the beakers.

7. Calculate the change in each bag's mass (final mass – initial mass) and the percent change $\left(\frac{\text{mass change}}{\text{initial mass}} \times 100\right)$. Record the values in the table below and use the data to answer the questions.

Table 1

Beaker	Bag Sol	Beaker Sol	Initial Bag Mass	Final Bag Mass	Mass Change	%Change
A	10%	1%				
B	10%	5%				
C	10%	10%				
D	10%	20%				
E	10%	40%				
F	1%	10%				
G	40%	10%				

Conclude and Apply

1. What happened to the mass of Bags A and B during the experiment?

_____

_____

_____

2. Were the concentrations of the solutions in Beakers A and B more than or less than the concentrations of the solutions inside the bags? Would you classify the solutions in the beakers as hypertonic, hypotonic, or isotonic relative to the solution inside the bag? (Refer to the *Background* section for more information.)

_____

_____

_____

3. Explain the changes observed in Bags A and B in terms of the concentrations of solutions inside and outside the bags and the movement of water.

_____

_____

_____

4. What happened to the mass of Bag C?

_____

_____

_____

Lab 1

Where did they drown? *continued*

5. How did the solution in Beaker C compare to the solution inside the bag? Would you classify it as hypertonic, hypotonic, or isotonic relative to the solution inside the bag?

_____

_____

_____

_____

_____

_____

6. Explain any changes observed in Bag C in terms of the concentrations of solutions inside and outside the bag and the movement of water.

_____

_____

_____

_____

_____

_____

_____

7. What happened to the masses of Bags D and E during the experiment?

_____

_____

_____

_____

_____

_____

8. Were the concentrations of the solutions in Beakers D and E more than or less than the concentrations of the solutions inside the bags? Would you classify the solutions in the beakers as hypertonic, hypotonic, or isotonic relative to the solution inside the bag? (Refer to the *Background* section for more information.)

_____

_____

_____

_____

_____

_____

_____

Lab 1 **Where did they drown?** *continued*

9. Explain the changes observed in Bags D and E in terms of the concentrations of solutions inside and outside the bags and the movement of water.

_____

_____

_____

_____

_____

_____

10. Beaker F represents a person who drowned in freshwater. The bag represents the lungs, and the solution in the beaker represents the blood. The 1% sucrose inside the bag approximates the total salt concentration in freshwater, while the 10% sucrose in the beaker approximates the total salt concentration in the blood. What happened to the mass of the bag? Did water move out of the bag or into the bag? What happened to the concentration of sucrose in the beaker? Explain.

_____

_____

_____

_____

_____

_____

11. Beaker G represents a person who drowned in salt water. The 40% sucrose inside the bag approximates the total salt concentration in salt water, while the 10% sucrose in the beaker approximates the total salt concentration in the blood. What happened to the mass of the bag? Did water move out of the bag or into the bag? What happened to the concentration of sucrose in the beaker? Explain.

_____

_____

_____

_____

_____

_____

_____

Lab 1

Where did they drown? *continued*

Analyze and Conclude

12. The following table contains the concentrations (in millimoles per liter) of various substances in the blood of the two drowning victims. Just as the term *dozen* refers to a specific number of things (12), the term *mole* refers to a specific number of particles (6.02×10^{23}). A millimole is $1/1000^{th}$ of a mole. When concentration is given in millimoles (or moles) per liter, higher numbers indicate more particles dissolved in the water—in the table below, higher concentrations of sodium, potassium, or chloride.

Table 2

Concentration (mmole/L)			
Substance	Man	Woman	Normal Values
Sodium	200	100	145
Potassium	10	2	5
Chloride	125	75	100

Where do you think each victim drowned? Explain your answer.

_____

_____

_____

_____

13. Should you look for murderers or did the victims drown accidentally? Explain your answer.

_____

_____

_____

_____

_____

_____

_____

Lab 2   How can you extract DNA from cells?

The Problem

The Biotech Foods Company is developing an improved strain of bananas through genetic engineering. In order to obtain DNA that they can examine and use, scientists working for the company must extract the DNA from banana cells in a way that does not destroy the DNA molecules. Conditions that can damage or destroy DNA molecules include exposure to heat, acids, and ultraviolet radiation. In this lab, you will follow a simple procedure for extracting DNA.

DNA Extraction Procedures for changing an organism's DNA through genetic engineering require DNA molecules. Therefore, the first step in most genetic engineering procedures is DNA extraction. First, the lipids and proteins that make up the cell's plasma membrane are dissolved, and the bonds between them are broken. Second, the lipids and proteins form complexes that are filtered out of solution, leaving the DNA behind in the liquid that passes through the filter. Third, the DNA molecules are made visible by adding alcohol to this liquid.

Everyday Materials

- ❏ blender
- ❏ banana (1)
- ❏ 5-oz plastic cups (2)
- ❏ color-free shampoo
- ❏ table salt
- ❏ plastic teaspoon
- ❏ #2 cone coffee filter

Lab Materials

- ❏ sealed (rubber stopper) test tube containing cold alcohol (95% ethanol or 91% isopropyl alcohol)
- ❏ pipette or dropper
- ❏ 270 mL distilled water

Safety

- Always wear safety goggles and a lab apron.
- Be careful when handling glass test tubes because the glass is fragile.
- Never eat or drink anything in the lab.
- Be sure to keep your hands away from your eyes and face in the science lab.
- Wash your hands thoroughly after each lab activity.

Procedure

1. Add 1 banana and 250 mL distilled water to the blender, replace the lid on the blender, and blend for 20 seconds. Do not put any objects into the blender while it is in operation.

2. To a 5-oz cup, add 1 teaspoon shampoo, 2 pinches salt, and 20 mL distilled water. To avoid foaming, stir slowly with a spoon until the salt and shampoo dissolve.

3. Add 3 heaping teaspoons of the banana mixture to the shampoo and salt solution. Stir gently for 10 minutes.

4. Place a #2 cone coffee filter inside the second 5-oz plastic cup. Fold the filter over the edge of the cup so that it does not touch the bottom.

5. Pour the solution from Step 3 into the filter and let it drain for several minutes.

6. Fill the pipette or dropper with filtrate and transfer it to the cold alcohol in the test tube.

7. Let the solution sit undisturbed for 3 minutes. Do not shake or stir the test tube. Observe as the banana DNA precipitates out. It will have the appearance of white, stringy mucus.

Lab 2 How can you extract DNA from cells?
continued

Cleanup and Disposal

1. Rinse, dry, and put away the test tube.

2. Dispose of all other leftover materials as instructed.

Data and Observations

In the space below, draw a sketch of the DNA strands.

Conclude and Apply

1. The purpose of the table salt in Step 2 of the *Procedure* was to enable the DNA strands to come together. What purpose do you think the shampoo serves?

   _____

   _____

   _____

   _____

2. Suppose you substituted distilled water for alcohol in the cold test tube in Step 6 of the *Procedure*. How do you think this would affect the outcome?

   _____

   _____

   _____

   _____

3. Could you extract DNA from cooked food to use in a genetic engineering procedure? Why or why not?

   _____

   _____

   _____

   _____

Analyze and Conclude

4. Explain why DNA extraction is the first step for many procedures in genetic engineering.

   _____

   _____

Lab 3 How can you transform cells with new DNA?

The Problem

Researchers are working to develop gene therapy for human genetic disorders, such as cystic fibrosis and diabetes mellitus. The goal of gene therapy is to give functional genes to people with nonfunctional genes. Researchers have genetically engineered animals, such as lab mice, as well as plants. Such engineering provides genes for resistance to pests or diseases.

Background

DNA Transformation The basic concept behind genetic engineering is removing a functional DNA fragment, or gene, from one organism and combining it with the DNA of another organism. When a cell takes up new DNA, the process is called transformation. Plasmids often are used in this process.

Plasmids Plasmids are small, circular pieces of DNA. They are found naturally in some species of bacteria and have two features that make them useful for DNA transfer.

One feature that makes plasmids useful is their ability to direct their own replication. When a plasmid enters a bacterial cell, it instructs the cell to make copies of plasmid DNA. The replication of plasmid DNA is independent of the replication of the bacterial host's DNA.

The second feature that makes plasmids useful is a genetic marker that allows bacteria carrying the plasmid to be distinguished from those that are not. Genes for antibiotic resistance are commonly used as genetic markers. After transformation, the bacteria are cultured with the antibiotic. Only those cells that have been transformed survive, because only they carry the gene for antibiotic resistance.

Preparing Bacterial Cells Bacterial cells will not normally take up plasmid DNA. Preparing cells to take up plasmid DNA involves incubating the bacteria in a buffer solution. Even when bacterial cells are prepared in such a manner, many of them will not take up plasmid DNA. Because plasmid DNA contains the Lux gene and a gene conferring resistance to antibiotics, only cells that take up plasmid DNA will tend to grow in the presence of an antibiotic. In this way, you can select for the cells that take up plasmid DNA.

In this lab, you will gain hands-on experience with genetic engineering methods. You will use these methods to transform nonglowing bacteria into glowing bacteria, due to a gene that makes them glow in the dark. This will allow you to observe the new phenotype of the genetically engineered bacteria. You will work with a plasmid that contains both a gene for antibiotic resistance and a gene called the Lux gene. The Lux gene causes successfully transformed cells to glow in the dark. In the instructions that follow, your teacher will provide you with a supply of E. coli cells that have been treated with a buffer solution to enable them to take up plasmid DNA. You will grow these cells on agar treated with ampicillin, an antibiotic.

Lab 3 How can you transform cells with new DNA? *continued*

Everyday Materials
❏ plastic container of ice
❏ marking pen
❏ straws (2)

Lab Materials
❏ 10-μL aliquot plasmid DNA (1)
❏ 100-μL aliquots competent *E. coli* cells (2)
❏ microcentrifuge tubes (2)
❏ incubator

❏ 100-μL aliquots Luria broth (2)
❏ plates of culture medium with ampicillin (2)
❏ micropipettes (2)
❏ protective gloves

❏ micropipettes (2)
❏ protective gloves

Safety

- Always wear gloves, goggles, and an apron.
- Handle the micropipets carefully. The glass is fragile.
- Although the bacteria should be harmless, wash your hands thoroughly after handling the bacterial cultures and after you complete the lab.
- Be sure to keep your hands away from your eyes and face in the science lab.
- Follow your teacher's instructions for disposal of lab materials.

Procedure

Part A: Preparing the Plasmid Culture

1. In a microcentrifuge tube, mix the 10-μL aliquot of plasmid DNA with one of the 100 μL aliquots of competent *E. coli* cells.

2. Incubate the microcentrifuge tube on ice for 15 minutes.

3. Remove the test tube from the ice and incubate it in the incubator at 42°C for 2 minutes.

4. Add 100 μL of Luria broth to the

microcentrifuge tube and mix.

5. Incubate at 37°C for 10 minutes (or hold the tube in a clenched fist for the same amount of time).

6. Label an agar plate containing ampicillin with your initials and the letters *LUX*, for Lux gene.

7. Pipette the contents of the tube onto the agar.

8. Fold a straw into a triangular shape and use it as a spreader to evenly distribute the bacteria over the surface of the agar, as shown in the figure below.

9. Discard the straw as directed by your teacher and thoroughly wash your hands.

Part B: Preparing the Control Culture

10. Add the other 100-μL aliquot of competent *E. coli* cells to the second microcentrifuge tube.

11. Incubate the microcentrifuge tube on ice for 15 minutes.

12. Remove the microcentrifuge tube from the ice and incubate it in the incubator at 42°C for 2 minutes.

13. Add 100 μL of Luria broth to the microcentrifuge tube and mix.

14. Incubate at 37°C for 10 minutes.

15. Label the second agar plate with your initials and the letters *CON*, for control.

16. With the clean micropipette, deposit the contents of the microcentrifuge tube onto the agar. Make sure you do not use the same micropipette that you used in Part A.

17. Fold the other straw into a triangular shape and use it to spread the bacteria over the surface of the agar. Do not use the same straw that you used in Part A.

18. Write a hypothesis about what you think will happen to the bacteria on the two agar plates.

Hypothesis: _____

_____

Copyright © by Glencoe/McGraw-Hill, a division of the McGraw-Hill Companies, Inc.

Lab 3 How can you transform cells with new DNA? *continued*

_____

_____

_____

Part C: Observing Bacterial Growth and Phenotypes

19. Incubate both plates overnight at 35°C, and then the next day at room temperature.

20. The following day, inspect the plates for bacterial growth. Record what you observe under *Data and Observations*.

Cleanup and Disposal

1. Wipe down your work surface as instructed by your teacher. Wash and dry all containers and equipment and return them to their proper places.

2.

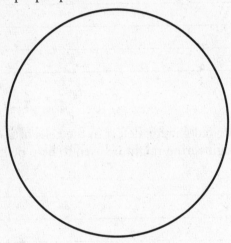

E. coli with plasmid DNA

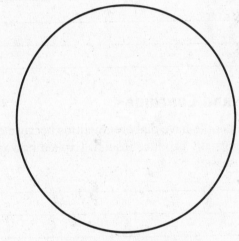

E. coli without plasmid DNA

Dispose of any leftover solutions as instructed.

Data and Observations

On the drawings below, sketch any bacterial growth that you observed on the two plates.

Conclude and Apply

Lab 3

How can you transform cells with new DNA? *continued*

1. Describe how the two cultures appeared to differ after incubating for a day at room temperature. Explain any differences you observed.

_____

_____

_____

_____

2. What was the purpose of the control culture in this procedure?

_____

_____

3. What was the reason for culturing the bacteria on agar plates containing ampicillin?

_____

_____

_____

_____

Analyze and Conclude

4. Some people have diabetes mellitus because of an inherited genetic defect in the cells of the pancreas that normally produce insulin. Explain how genetic engineering might be used to help people with this disease.

_____

_____

_____

_____

_____

_____

_____

Lab 4
How can you transcribe and translate a gene?

The Problem

Scientists have identified many of the tens of thousands of genes in the human genome. One application of this knowledge is the production of human proteins by genetically engineered bacteria. Insulin and some other vital human proteins cannot be artificially synthesized outside of living cells. However, genes for human proteins can be inserted into living bacteria and large quantities of these human proteins can be produced for medical use.

Bacteria are able to "read" human genes and synthesize human proteins because the same genetic code is found in all organisms. In this lab, you will use the genetic code to simulate the synthesis of protein segments.

Background

Genetic Code The genetic code is the relationship between the sequence of nucleotide bases in DNA molecules and the sequence of amino acids in proteins. There are four different bases found in DNA and 20 different amino acids found in proteins. Groups of three bases, called codons, code for individual amino acids.

Transcription Cells read genes and produce the correct strings of amino acids that form proteins using the information in the genetic code. This is a two-step process. The first step, transcription, involves copying the DNA sequence of the gene into messenger RNA (mRNA). Like DNA, RNA contains four nucleotide bases. However, in RNA, the base uracil (U) replaces the base thymine (T).

Before the information in DNA can be decoded, a small portion of the DNA double helix must be uncoiled. A strand of mRNA is then synthesized that is complementary to one strand of the DNA. The mRNA molecule carries the information for making a protein from the cell's nucleus to the cytoplasm, where protein synthesis takes place.

Translation The second step in protein production is translation. Recall that groups of three bases are called codons, and codons code for

individual amino acids, as shown in the table on the next page. The table is based on the mRNA sequence, so the base thymine (T) is replaced with the base uracil (U).

As you can see from the table, some amino acids have more than one codon, but each codon codes for just one amino acid. The codon AUG, which codes for the amino acid methionine, is a signal to start protein synthesis. The three codons UAA, UAG, and UGA do not code for any amino acids. Instead, each is a signal to end protein synthesis.

In the cytoplasm, the mRNA binds to a ribosome, where the message is translated into a sequence of amino acids. The amino acids that are incorporated into the protein are carried by relatively small RNA molecules known as transfer RNA, or tRNA. At one end of each tRNA molecule is a specific sequence of three nucleotides, complementary to the mRNA codon and called an anticodon, that can bind to the mRNA. At the other end of the tRNA molecule is the amino acid encoded by the anticodon. Only the information contained up to the stop codon (UAA, UAG, or UGA) in the mRNA molecule is used to produce the amino acid sequence. Starting with the start codon, the ribosome reads sets of three nucleotides at a time until a stop codon is reached.

Lab 4 — How can you transcribe and translate a gene? *continued*

	U	C	A	G	
U	UUU=Phe	UCU=Ser	UAU=Tyr	UGU=Cys	U
	UUC=Phe	UCC=Ser	UAC=Tyr	UGC=Cys	C
	UUA=Leu	UCA=Ser	UAA=stop	UGA=stop	A
	UUG=Leu	UCG=Ser	UAG=stop	UGG=Trp	G
C	CUU=Leu	CCU=Pro	CAU=His	CGU=Arg	U
	CUC=Leu	CCC=Pro	CAC=His	CGC=Arg	C
	CUA=Leu	CCA=Pro	CAA=Gln	CGA=Arg	A
	CUG=Leu	CCG=Pro	CAG=Gln	CGG=Arg	G
A	AUU=Ile	ACU=Thr	AAU=Asn	AGU=Ser	U
	AUC=Ile	ACC=Thr	AAC=Asn	AGC=Ser	C
	AUA=Ile	ACA=Thr	AAA=Lys	AGA=Arg	A
	AUG=Met	ACG=Thr	AAG=Lys	AGG=Arg	G
G	GUU=Val	GCU=Ala	GAU=Asp	GGU=Gly	U
	GUC=Val	GCC=Ala	GAC=Asp	GGC=Gly	C
	GUA=Val	GCA=Ala	GAA=Glu	GGA=Gly	A
	GUG=Val	GCG=Ala	GAG=Glu	GGG=Gly	G

Key

RNA Bases:
A = adenine, C = cytosine,
G = guanine, U = uracil

Amino Acids:
Phe = phenylalanine,
Leu = leucine,
Ile = isoleucine,
Met = methionine,
Val = valine,
Ser = serine,
Pro = proline,
Thr = threonine,
Ala = alanine,
Tyr = tyrosine,
His = histidine,
Gln = glutamine,
Asn = asparagine,
Lys = lysine,
Asp = aspartic acid,
Glu = glutamic acid,
Cys = cysteine,
Trp = tryptophan,
Arg = arginine,
Gly = glycine

Procedure

Part A: Transcribing and Translating Mystery DNA Sequences

1. You have been given two mystery DNA sequences, shown under *Data and Observations*. One of them codes for some of the amino acids in a known human protein. Transcribe and translate the mystery DNA sequences to identify the amino acid sequence encoded in each, following steps 2–4. Record your work under *Data and Observations*.

2. First, transcribe each DNA sequence by writing the corresponding sequence of complementary bases in the mRNA molecule.

3. Then, translate each mRNA sequence into a complementary sequence of tRNA anticodons.

4. Finally, use the genetic code to translate the mRNA sequence into the correct sequence of amino acids.

Part B: Translating and Transcribing DNA Sequences for Known Hemoglobins

5. Repeat steps 2–4 to determine the sequence of the first nine amino acids encoded in the DNA for normal hemoglobin (normal Hb). Record your results under *Data and Observations*.

6. A point mutation in the seventh codon for normal hemoglobin produces sickle-cell hemoglobin (Hb S). A change in a single nucleotide base results in the amino acid valine in this position. Record the sequence of the first nine amino acids in hemoglobin S under *Data and Observations*.

7. There are many other known hemoglobin variants, including hemoglobin C (Hb C), which has lysine instead of glutamic acid in position seven, and hemoglobin G (Hb G), which has glycine instead of glutamic acid in position eight. Record the sequences of the first nine amino acids in hemoglobins C and G under *Data and Observations*.

Data and Observations

Mystery DNA sequence #1

TAC	CAT	GTG	GAA	TGA	GGA	CTC	CCT	TTC
1	2	3	4	5	6	7	8	9

mRNA #1

1	2	3	4	5	6	7	8	9

tRNA #1

1	2	3	4	5	6	7	8	9

Amino acid sequence #1

1	2	3	4	5	6	7	8	9

Mystery DNA sequence #2

TAC	CAC	GAC	TGC	GGT	CCG	CTC	GTG	TTC
1	2	3	4	5	6	7	8	9

mRNA #2

1	2	3	4	5	6	7	8	9

tRNA #2

1	2	3	4	5	6	7	8	9

Amino acid sequence #2

1	2	3	4	5	6	7	8	9

DNA sequence normal hb

TAC	CAT	GTG	GAA	TGA	GGA	CTC	CTC	TTC
1	2	3	4	5	6	7	8	9

mRNA normal hb

1	2	3	4	5	6	7	8	9

tRNA normal hb

1	2	3	4	5	6	7	8	9

Amino acid sequence normal hb

1	2	3	4	5	6	7	8	9

Lab 4

How can you transcribe and translate a gene? *continued*

Amino acid sequence Hb S

1	2	3	4	5	6	7	8	9

Amino acid sequence Hb C

1	2	3	4	5	6	7	8	9

Amino acid sequence Hb G

1	2	3	4	5	6	7	8	9

Analyze and Conclude

1. Compare the sequences of amino acids for the two mystery DNA samples with the sequences of amino acids in the four known hemoglobin molecules. Which mystery amino acid sequence is a match for a hemoglobin molecule? Which hemoglobin molecule is it?

_____
_____
_____

2. Identify the point mutations that would change the DNA sequence for normal hemoglobin into a DNA sequence for hemoglobins S, C, and G. Remember: a point mutation is a change in a single nucleotide base.

_____
_____
_____

3. If the final segment, CTC CTC TTC, of the normal hemoglobin DNA sequence underwent a point mutation to become CTC CTT TTC, would it affect the resulting protein? Explain your answer.

_____
_____
_____

4. Predict how a mutation in the seventh codon of normal hemoglobin, changing it from CTC to ATC, would affect the protein being synthesized.

_____
_____
_____

5. Explain the significance of a genetic code that is consistent between organisms to biotechnology.

_____
_____
_____

FORENSICS AND BIOTECHNOLOGY

Lab 5
How can you diagnose genotypes using DNA?

The Problem

Sickle-cell anemia is a disease caused by a mutation in the gene that codes for β-globin (beta-globin), one of the two types of polypeptide chains that make up the hemoglobin molecule. The two β-globin alleles that are relevant to sickle-cell anemia are abbreviated A (normal allele) and S (sickle-cell allele). In general, only people who are homozygous for the mutation (SS) have the disease. People who are heterozygous (AS) are called carriers. They have one normal and one sickle-cell gene and usually do not have symptoms of sickle-cell anemia. However, if two heterozygotes marry, their children can have the disease. Therefore, it is important to be able to diagnose suspected carriers. In this lab, you will learn how to diagnose sickle-cell genotypes using a biotechnology method called DNA restriction enzyme analysis.

Background

Cutting DNA into Fragments DNA molecules are too large to be analyzed without cutting them into smaller fragments. This can be done with restriction enzymes. There are more than 100 known restriction enzymes, and each cuts DNA at one specific nucleotide sequence.

Separating DNA Fragments To analyze DNA fragments, they must be separated. This can be done with gel electrophoresis. In this procedure, a mixture of DNA fragments is deposited at one end of a porous gel that is similar to a slice of gelatin. An electric current produces negative and positive ends in the gel, and this bipolarity causes the DNA fragments to move across the gel. Because DNA is negatively charged, it moves toward the positive end. However, smaller fragments move faster and travel farther across the gel in a given length of time. Based on their size, the DNA fragments create a pattern of bands on the gel, as shown in **Figure 1**. These bands can be compared with other, known samples of DNA. Matching them with known samples allows researchers to identify the size of the DNA fragments.

Figure 1

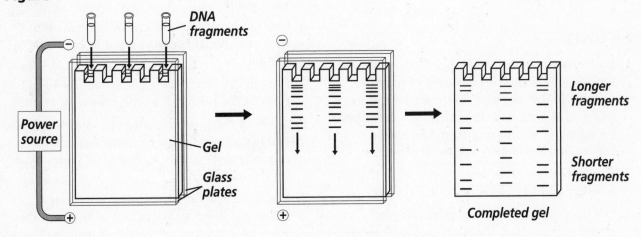

Lab 5   How can you diagnose genotypes using DNA? *continued*

Diagnosis of Sickle-cell Genotypes A restriction enzyme called Mst II recognizes and cuts DNA at the nucleotide sequence CCTGAGG. This sequence appears in the gene that codes for normal β-globin. However, the mutation that causes sickle-cell anemia changes the A to T in this sequence. The new nucleotide sequence, CCTGTGG, not only causes sickle-cell anemia, but also loss of the recognition site for the restriction enzyme Mst II, which means the enzyme will not cut the DNA at this site.

As a result, DNA fragments cut from people who are homozygous for the mutation (SS) will be longer than those cut from people who are homozygous for the normal allele (AA). While DNA fragments from an SS individual will be longer than those from an AA individual, an AS individual will have both long and short fragments. These fragments can be separated with electrophoresis and identified by their characteristic banding patterns when compared with known samples.

Everyday Materials

❏ clear glass plate

Lab Materials

❏ test tubes containing simulated DNA fragments (7)
❏ gel cassette for electrophoresis

❏ P-20 micropipette with 7 tips
❏ 150-mL 1% TAE buffer
❏ gel electrophoresis box
❏ protective gloves

Safety

- Always wear gloves and goggles.
- Be sure to keep your hands away from your eyes and face in the science lab.
- Use power cords with caution.
- Wear an apron to protect your clothes from the dye in the samples.

Procedure

1. From your teacher, obtain four "DNA" samples for one family and also one each of the three known "DNA" samples. The code for the seven tubes is: M = mother, F = father, T = teenager, I = infant, N = known normal, C = known carrier, and S = known sickle-cell patient.

2. Under *Data and Observations*, record in the key whether you have Family #1 or Family #2.

3. Obtain a cassette of gel and place it in the electrophoresis box. The wells should be facing up at the end with the black (negative) electrode.

4. Add enough 1% TAE buffer to the gel box so that the gel is covered by about 1 or 2 mm of buffer. Place the lid on the box.

5. Using a P-20 micropipette set to 8 μL, load each of the seven DNA samples into a separate well. Care should be taken not to damage the wells with the micropipette tip. Take turns loading with the other students in your group. Use a new micropipette tip for each sample.

6. Use the key under *Data and Observations* to indicate which sample you put in each lane of the gel.

7. Plug in the electrical leads, set at 120 V, and turn on the power. Run the gel for 10 minutes.

8. Turn off the power, unplug the electrical leads, and open the gel box. Remove the gel and carefully slide it onto a clear glass plate. Pour off the extra buffer.

9. Place the dish on white paper for better contrast. Observe the pattern of bands in the gel. Color this pattern in the drawing of the gel under *Data and Observations*.

Lab 5   How can you diagnose genotypes using DNA? *continued*

Cleanup and Disposal

1. Dispose of the gel and buffer as instructed by your teacher.

2. Return all equipment to its proper place.

Data and Observations

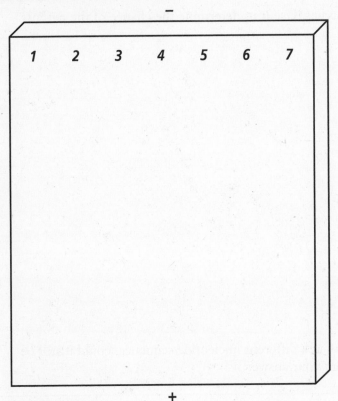

Key: Family # _____

1 = _____   3 = _____   5 = _____   7 = _____

2 = _____   4 = _____   6 = _____

Conclude and Apply

1. What properties of the two dyes used in the lab make them suitable for the simulation of DNA restriction analysis?

_____

_____

_____

_____

Lab 5 How can you diagnose genotypes using DNA? *continued*

2. Based on your restriction analysis, what are the genotypes of each family member?

_____

_____

_____

_____

_____

3. Make a Punnett square for the parents' genotypes. Use it to determine the chance of the parents having a child with sickle-cell anemia.

Analyze and Conclude

4. If the Mst II enzyme recognized and cut DNA at a different nucleotide sequence, could it still be used to diagnose sickle-cell genotypes? Explain your answer.

_____

_____

_____

_____

_____

_____

_____

_____

FORENSICS AND BIOTECHNOLOGY

Lab 6
How can genetically engineered plants be multiplied?

The Problem

Dr. Ramirez has used genetic engineering in an attempt to make African violets more resistant to a fungal disease. First, she isolated DNA from a bacterial species that resists the fungus. Then, using a particle gun, a device used to insert new DNA into cells such as plant cells and bacteria, she "shot" the bacterial DNA into the cells of tiny pieces of African violet leaves. Now that the transfer of DNA is complete, she must grow new plants from the tiny pieces of modified leaf tissue. How can this be done?

The answer is micropropagation. In this careful procedure, which is explained in the following paragraphs, tiny pieces of plant tissue are disinfected and then cultured in a sterile medium until they start to produce new shoots. In this lab, you will use micropropagation to produce new shoots from tiny pieces of African violet leaves.

Background

DNA Transfer New genetic traits can be incorporated into an organism by directly transferring DNA from another organism. DNA can be transferred to plants by "shooting" them with a particle gun or by infecting plant tissues with a bacterium that then incorporates part of its DNA into the DNA of the host plant. In both methods, the DNA is transferred to a tiny fragment of plant tissue or a small mass of plant cells. Once the DNA has been transferred, the only way to regenerate new plants from such small pieces of tissue or clumps of cells is with tissue culture using micropropagation methods.

Micropropagation Micropropagation differs from all other plant propagation techniques in requiring aseptic conditions, conditions that are sterile or free of contamination by microorganisms, in order to be successful. The growing medium promotes the growth of bacteria and fungi spores, which are commonly found on surfaces and in the air. If the plant tissue cultures are contaminated by these organisms, they will grow rampantly and destroy or infect the plant tissues in the same culture.

Maintaining Aseptic Conditions To maintain aseptic conditions during the micropropagation process, it is necessary to keep all dust particles (which may contain bacteria) and spores of fungi away from the work area. This can be done in various ways. In large labs, the work usually is performed under a hood that filters these contaminants out of the work area. A simpler, but still relatively effective, way to reduce the chance of contamination is to spray the work area, hands, instruments, and all other objects in the work area with a 70% ethanol solution before the work begins.

To cut down on air movement that might transfer contaminants into the work area once it has been disinfected with ethanol, the work can be done inside a new large, clear plastic bag, which should be relatively sterile, or inside an aquarium or cardboard box that has been lined with aluminum foil and sprayed with ethanol. It is important to keep traffic around the work area to a minimum to reduce air movement and the potential for contamination.

Lab 6 — How can genetically engineered plants be multiplied? *continued*

Everyday Materials

- ❏ prepackaged African violet medium
- ❏ table sugar
- ❏ fresh African violet leaves (2)
- ❏ 0.1% detergent solution
- ❏ 10% bleach solution
- ❏ sterile razor blade
- ❏ scissors
- ❏ marking pen

Lab Materials

- ❏ protective gloves
- ❏ 70% ethanol in spray bottle
- ❏ distilled water
- ❏ 250-mL beaker
- ❏ stirring rod
- ❏ pH meter or paper
- ❏ dropper
- ❏ NaOH and HCl (as needed to adjust pH)

- ❏ 250-mL bottle
- ❏ agar powder
- ❏ sterile petri dishes (5)
- ❏ 250-mL or larger glass jar with screw-cap lid
- ❏ 1 L sterile water
- ❏ sterile forceps
- ❏ parafilm

Safety

- Always wear gloves, goggles, and a lab apron.
- Use caution when handling the razor blade and scissors.
- Make sure the ethanol is never near an open flame.
- Be careful to avoid burns when handling hot water or working with a hot plate.
- Avoid splashing bleach solution onto your clothes because it will remove the color.
- Be sure to keep your hands away from your eyes and face in the science lab.
- Never eat or drink anything in the lab.
- Wash your hands thoroughly after each lab activity.

Procedure

Part A: Creating an Aseptic Environment

1. Put on a pair of protective gloves. Spray them with 70% ethanol before starting the procedure, and then respray them whenever you touch any nonsterile surface or material throughout the remainder of the procedure.

2. Spray your work surface with 70% ethanol. Also, spray all containers before placing them on the work surface as you carry out the procedure.

Part B: Preparing the Culture Medium

3. Place about 50 mL of distilled water, 0.58 g of prepackaged African violet medium, and 3.75 g of table sugar into a 250-mL beaker.

4. Add distilled water to bring the solution up to 100 mL. Stir until the sugar and African violet medium are dissolved.

5. Check the pH using a pH meter or paper. Add a few drops of NaOH or HCl as supplied by your teacher as needed to bring the pH between 5.6 and 5.8.

6. Add more distilled water to bring the solution up to 125 mL.

7. Pour the solution into a 250-mL bottle and add 1.0 g of agar powder.

8. Keeping the cap loose on the bottle, sterilize it by placing it in boiling water for 30 minutes.

9. Remove the bottle from the hot water bath and gently swirl the medium to mix the agar until it is completely dissolved.

10. After the medium cools to about 50°C, pour about 25 mL into each of four sterile petri dishes. Store the dishes in their sleeves in the refrigerator until you need them in Part D of the *Procedure*.

Lab 6 How can genetically engineered plants be multiplied? *continued*

Part C: Disinfecting the Leaves

11. Put the African violet leaves in the screw-cap jar and half-fill the jar with 0.1% detergent solution. Cap the jar tightly and gently agitate it for 3 minutes.

12. Pour off the detergent solution and rinse the leaves and jar with cool tap water.

13. Repeat step 11, substituting 10% bleach solution for detergent solution and gently agitate it for 10 minutes.

14. Pour off the bleach solution into the sink while keeping the lid loosely in place over the jar. Be careful not to pour out the leaves along with the bleach solution. The leaves should now be sterile. From this point on, prevent them from becoming contaminated by using only sterile water and sterile tools on them.

15. Spray the outside of the jar with 70% ethanol and place it on your sterile work surface.

16. Remove the lid from the jar and pour sterile water over the leaves until the jar is about half-full. Replace the lid and gently shake the jar for 2 minutes. Carefully pour off the rinse water into the sink without touching the leaves or removing them from the jar.

17. Repeat step 16 three times for a total of four sterile water rinses.

Part D: Preparing Leaf Tissue Cultures

18. Using the forceps, place the leaves on the remaining empty sterile petri dish. Hold the leaves with the forceps while you use the razor blade to cut them into squares about 1.5 cm on a side.

19. Place two or three strips of leaf into a dish of medium. Gently press the pieces against the medium with the forceps. Replace the cover on the dish and wrap it with a piece of parafilm, stretching the film to seal it. You and your partner should each prepare two dishes in this way. Label your two dishes with your initials and number them *one* and *two*.

Part E: Growing and Monitoring the Cultures

20. Place both dishes under lights in the place provided by your teacher.

21. Check the dishes after a few days for evidence of growth. Any dishes with fuzzy or slimy growth visible on them have been contaminated by fungi or bacteria and should be discarded as directed by your teacher.

22. Continue to check the dishes once a week for at least five weeks and record your observations each time.

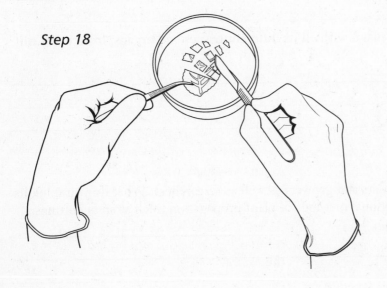

Step 18

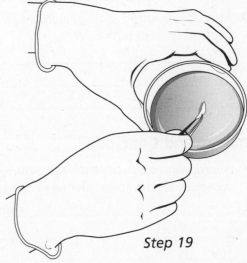

Step 19

Lab 6 How can genetically engineered plants be multiplied? *continued*

Cleanup and Disposal

1. Rinse and dry all containers and equipment and return them to their proper place.

2. Dispose of any leftover solutions or culture medium according to your teacher's instructions.

Data and Observations

Each week when you observe your petri dishes, record the date and dish number and draw a sketch of what you see, using a circle like the one shown below to represent the perimeter of the petri dish.

Date: _____

Dish Number: _____

Conclude and Apply

1. Why is it crucial to maintain aseptic conditions when carrying out micropropagation of plants? What is likely to happen if aseptic conditions are not maintained?

_____
_____
_____

2. Explain the role that plant micropropagation plays in genetic engineering.

_____
_____
_____

3. How is it possible to regenerate a new plant, with all its different tissues and organs, from just a tiny piece of leaf tissue?

_____
_____
_____

Analyze and Conclude

4. Micropropagation is used by plant breeders and growers as well as researchers. What do you think its commercial advantages are over conventional methods of plant propagation, such as stem cuttings?

_____
_____
_____

Lab 7 When did she die?

Your medical examiner team has been given the following case to review. It is your job to determine whether the victim died accidentally and what the time of death was. Study the details and complete the medical examiner's report that follows.

The Problem

The victim was found in her home at 10:00 A.M. on Saturday morning by her sister, with whom she was supposed to go jogging. The sister promptly called the police who then notified you, the medical examiner. You noted the following:

- The victim was lying facedown at the bottom of the stairs, facing away from the stairs. The sister indicated the victim was dressed in the clothes she had worn to dinner the night before.

- The victim had no pulse.

- The body was cold to the touch, but the internal temperature, which was measured at 10:30 A.M., was 27°C (room temperature was 20°C).

- Her neck was apparently fractured, and she appeared to have sustained head injuries.

- There were purplish marks on the front of her shoulders and neck; the marks did not change color when touched.

- Her entire body was stiff.

- The victim's eyes were open and cloudy with a thin film.

Additional Police Notes   The victim had eaten dinner with her sister at 5:00 P.M. the night before (Friday evening). At dinner, they had agreed to meet at the victim's townhouse at 10:00 A.M. Saturday morning to go jogging. The sister returned to her own home at 11:00 P.M., but she was not sure when the victim returned to her townhouse after dinner. Neighbors did not recall seeing the victim return to her townhouse.

When you performed an autopsy on the victim later that day, you noted that she died of a broken neck and subsequent asphyxiation. The victim was 5 feet 8 inches tall and weighed 130 pounds, her stomach was empty, and her small intestine was full. Your job is to provide police with the time of death.

Background

When a body is discovered, one of the first things that a medical examiner must do is determine the time of death. The medical examiner uses several indicators to help establish the time of death, including body temperature, rigor mortis, discoloration (livor mortis or lividity), and the appearance of the eyes.

Body Temperature When a person dies, the body immediately begins to cool. On average, the body temperature drops at a rate of 0.75°C per hour for the first 12 hours. After 12 hours, the rate of cooling slows by about one half (approximately 0.4°C per hour) until the body reaches ambient temperature, the temperature of the environment. The rate of cooling is also affected by the following factors:

- *Air temperature* – A body will cool faster on a cold winter night than on a warm summer night.
- *Body fat* – Fat tends to insulate the body, so the more fat a person has, the slower the body cools after death.
- *Clothing* – Clothing also insulates the body, so heavy clothing will slow the rate of cooling.
- *Water* – A body in water cools much faster than one in air. Therefore, it is difficult to use body temperature to estimate the time of death for a victim found in the water.

Rigor Mortis At the time of death, the body's muscles are relaxed. However, within 1–2 hours, the muscles begin to stiffen as their stores of adenosine triphosphate (ATP) become exhausted. This stiffening is known as rigor mortis. Rigor mortis begins with the muscles of the face, jaws, and neck, proceeds down the body through the upper arms and torso, and ends with the legs. This process is complete within 8–12 hours after death. As the muscles begin to break down, they begin to relax in the same order as they stiffened. By 24–48 hours after death, the body is totally relaxed again.

Livor Mortis (Lividity) Within 1–2 hours after death, the blood settles into the lowest parts of the body (parts that are closest to or resting on the ground) due to gravity. The red blood cells settle out and break down into the tissues, leaving purplish marks that later become yellow (due to the breakdown of hemoglobin). The color (lividity) becomes fixed in the tissue within 6–8 hours after death. If a body is moved after this time, then the position of the purplish marks may not agree with the position in which the body is found. Finally, if skin appears discolored, but turns white when touched, then lividity has not been fixed and death probably occurred more than 2 hours, but less than 10 hours ago.

Appearance of the Eyes If the eyes remain open at the time of death, then a thin film will appear on them as they begin to dry out. As the blood cells within the body break down, they release potassium. Potassium enters the eyes and causes them to appear cloudy. This process takes approximately 2–3 hours after death; however, if the eyes remain closed after death, then the process takes much longer (approximately 24 hours).

Stomach Contents After you eat, the process of digestion takes place. Digestion begins in the stomach. It takes about 4–6 hours for the stomach to empty its contents into the small intestine. Finally, it takes approximately 12 hours for the food to leave the small intestine. As a rule of thumb:

- Undigested stomach contents—death occurred 0–2 hours after the meal
- Stomach empty—death occurred 4–6 hours after the meal
- Small intestines empty—death occurred 12 hours or more after the meal

Materials

❑ ruler

❑ graph paper

❑ your Biology textbook

❑ calculator

❑ the instructions for this activity

Conclude and Apply

Review

1. What is the normal body temperature in degrees Celsius?

   _____

2. What biological process allows humans, mammals, and birds to maintain high body temperatures?

   _____

3. Research and explain briefly the role of ATP in muscle contraction.

   _____

   _____

   _____

   _____

   _____

4. Explain the path that food takes through the digestive system in your body.

   _____

   _____

   _____

   _____

   _____

Medical Examiner's Report

5. Based on the background information about the average temperature decrease after death, calculate the body temperature for each hour up to 24 hours after death.

Hour	Body Temp. (°C)	Hour	Body Temp. (°C)	Hour	Body Temp. (°C)
1		9		17	
2		10		18	
3		11		19	
4		12		20	
5		13		21	
6		14		22	
7		15		23	
8		16		24	

6. Plot the data for temperature versus time after death on graph paper.

7. Based on the body temperature of the victim, how long has it been since the victim died?

_____

8. Estimate the time of death using body temperature.

_____

9. Based on the observations of rigor mortis, how long has the victim been dead?

_____

10. Where was lividity observed on the body? Was it fixed? How long ago did she die? Was the victim found in the position that she died or was her body moved? Explain your answer.

_____

_____

_____

11. Based on the appearance of her eyes, how long ago did she die? Explain your answer.

_____

_____

_____

12. Based on the examination of her digestive system, how long after a meal did the victim die? Explain.

_____

_____

_____

Analyze and Conclude

13. Based on all of the evidence available, estimate the time of death for the victim. Explain your answer.

_____

_____

_____

14. Was the victim's death an accident? Explain your answer.

_____

_____

_____

Lab 8 A Sweet Season

The Problem

The boys' basketball team has been practicing long hours and playing exhausting games all season. Their hard work has paid off. They will be playing in the state championship in two weeks. However, two of the starting players, Jorge and Kyle, have reported to the team doctor. Both boys (age 17) have been complaining about fatigue and muscle weakness and are worried about being able to play their best in the championship.

Listed below are the symptoms the players shared with the doctor.

Jorge: sleepy in classes; muscle weakness; increased appetite; drinks plenty of fluids; occasional dizzy spells after heavy exertion; increased urination (not excessive)

Kyle: sleepy in classes, especially after lunch; muscle weakness; increased appetite, almost excessive; drinks plenty of fluids, but always feels thirsty; frequent dizzy spells after long practices or heavy exertion; urinates frequently; 15 pound weight loss

Both boys had pre-season physical exams and were healthy. However, both boys have a family history of diabetes, a disease in which the body does not effectively respond to the levels of glucose, a very important type of sugar, in the blood. The result is dangerously high concentrations of glucose in the blood. Jorge's father developed diabetes at age 50 and is currently managing it by dieting. Kyle's grandfather had diabetes all of his life. He had to inject insulin daily, developed complications from diabetes, and died at age 55.

Because the symptoms and histories indicate that one or both boys may have diabetes, a glucose tolerance test is ordered to diagnose the disease.

Glucose Tolerence Test On the day of the test, each boy does not eat breakfast. During the test, each boy drinks a concentrated glucose solution (50–100 g glucose) and has blood drawn every 30 minutes for 2.5 hours. The blood samples are spun in a centrifuge to separate plasma from blood cells. A portion of each sample is sent to an outside lab, where the insulin and glucose contents in each plasma sample will be measured.

You are a technician in the lab that will measure the blood glucose by using a glucose test strip. The strip contains an absorbent pad that contains two enzymes, *glucose oxidase* and *peroxidase*, and a color indicator. When a blood sample is applied to the pad, glucose oxidase converts glucose to gluconic acid and hydrogen peroxide. Peroxidase then reacts the hydrogen peroxide with the color indicator, which varies in color from light green to brown depending upon the amount of glucose in the sample. Light green indicates lower glucose concentrations, while dark brown indicates higher concentrations. You will compare the color of the strip to a color scale on the bottle to determine the glucose concentration in the sample. You will then graph and analyze the data to make a preliminary diagnosis.

Lab 8 A Sweet Season, continued

Everyday Materials

❏ tissues
❏ watch with a second hand display or stopwatch
❏ ruler
❏ graph paper

Lab Materials

❏ labeled tubes (12) containing simulated plasma samples (5 mL) from each boy (before, 0.5, 1, 1.5, 2, 2.5 h)
❏ glucose test strips (12)
❏ copy of the test strip color chart (if you do not have a copy, see the description in the *Procedure*)

Safety

- Never taste or drink anything in the lab.
- Be sure to keep your hands away from your eyes and face in the science lab.
- Wash your hands thoroughly after each lab activity.

Procedure

1. To measure glucose in each sample with the test strips, do the following:

   a. Take a strip and hold it by the end opposite the test area.

   b. Dip the strip into the tube containing the sample and remove it immediately (draw the edge of the strip against the rim of the test tube to remove any excess fluid).

   c. Start the stopwatch and compare the color of the strip to the color scale exactly 30 seconds after wetting the strip (ignore any color changes that occur after 30 seconds).

   d. Note the reading on the data table.

   e. Repeat the procedure with the next sample and continue until you have tested all of the samples.

Plasma Glucose Concentration (mg/dL)		
Time (h)	Jorge	Kyle
Before (0)		
0.5		
1.0		
1.5		
2.0		
2.5		

Test Strip Color Scale	
Color	Glucose (mg/dL)
Aqua	<100
Light Green	100
Green	250
Olive	500
Light Brown	1000
Dark Brown	≥ 2000

2. On graph paper, plot the data for each boy on the same graph. Plot the plasma glucose concentration on the *y*-axis and time on the *x*-axis.

Use your data to answer the following questions. You may also wish to have your textbook and some additional information about diabetes available.

Conclude and Apply

1. Was the blood glucose concentration the same in each boy prior to the test (i.e. fasting blood glucose)? If not, whose blood glucose concentration was higher?

_____

_____

_____

_____

Lab
8   **A Sweet Season,** *continued*

2. Describe the changes in blood glucose that occur over time in each boy.

_____

_____

_____

3. How does glucose that you eat get into your bloodstream? In your answer, describe the organs that it must pass through.

_____

_____

_____

4. Does the pattern of the changes in blood glucose that you observed in the boys make sense in light of your answer to question 3? Explain why or why not.

_____

_____

_____

_____

5. Whose blood glucose concentration is more stable (i.e. controlled), Jorge's or Kyle's?

_____

_____

_____

Analyze and Conclude

6. Based on the information that you have so far, do either of the boys have diabetes? If so, which boy and how did you make that conclusion?

_____

_____

_____

_____

7. Obtain a copy of the insulin report from your teacher and look over the data. Describe how insulin levels change with time during the test for each boy.

_____

_____

_____

8. How do the changes in plasma insulin concentration correlate with the changes in blood glucose?

_____

_____

_____

9. Based on the information that you now have, do either of the boys have diabetes? Support your conclusion.

_____

_____

_____

10. Based on your data, what does insulin do to blood glucose levels?

_____

_____

_____

11. Which boy might be better able to withstand a long period without food? Why?

_____

_____

_____

12. If either of the boys has diabetes, explain how the disease accounts for his symptoms. If neither of the boys has diabetes, then what might cause their symptoms? (You will need to obtain information about diabetes.)

_____

_____

_____

_____

13. What treatment might you recommend for each boy? Why?

_____

_____

_____

_____

_____

Lab 9 Use Blood Types to Help Solve a Crime

The Problem

Some school property was vandalized, and a few drops of blood were found at the scene of the crime. The detectives investigating the incident think that the blood came from the perpetrator of the crime, who apparently was slightly injured during the vandalism. The detectives have gathered a group of suspects who were all on school property when the crime was committed. However, the only hard evidence is the blood found at the scene. The detectives want to rule out as many of the innocent suspects as possible on the basis of the blood evidence. In this lab, you will act as a lab technician, analyzing a sample of blood from a suspect to determine the blood type. Each one of your classmates will analyze a sample from a different suspect. Then, you and your classmates will compare the blood types of your samples with the type of blood found at the crime scene in order to narrow down the field of suspects.

Background

Using Blood Typing in Forensics Blood typing is frequently used in forensic investigations. A very small quantity of blood can easily be tested for dozens of genetically controlled traits that have little, if any, environmental influences on their expression. This means that if you know a person's phenotype for these traits, you also know his or her genotype, or genetic identity.

There are hundreds of known human blood-group systems in addition to the familiar ABO and Rh, or rhesus, blood groups. Each system is based on classes of antigenic molecules on the surface of the red blood cells. An antigenic molecule is recognized by the body's immune system as a foreign substance, to which it reacts by producing an antibody. Classification, or typing, of a person's blood to determine which molecular forms are present on the red blood cell depends on antigen-antibody reactions.

Agglutination Reaction If you take serum from a person of known blood type and add it to a drop of blood to be typed, one of two things will happen. The serum may mix freely with the red cells with no noticeable change, or the mixture may agglutinate, that is, the red blood cells clump together, producing a readily observable change as shown in **Figure 1**.

ABO Blood Type There are two common antigenic substances in the ABO blood group, A and B. The O type is not associated with an antigen, which means it is not recognized as a foreign substance by anyone's immune system—even people who do not have O type blood. Antibodies to type A antigen normally are found in the serum of people without the A antigen (that is, in people with type B or type O blood). These anti-A antibodies cause type A cells to agglutinate if they are mixed together. If a blood sample is agglutinated only by anti-A antibodies and not by anti-B antibodies, then the sample is type A, as shown in **Table 1**. Agglutination reactions that identify blood types B, AB, and O also are shown in **Table 1**.

Figure 1

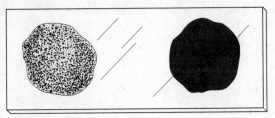

Agglutination (+)   **No Agglutination (–)**

Table 1

ABO Blood Type	Anti-A Reaction (+/–)	Anti-B Reaction (+/–)
A	+	–
B	–	+
AB	+	+
O	–	–

Use Blood Types to Help Solve a Crime, *continued*

Rhesus Blood Type Rhesus blood types have only one common antigen associated with them. It is often referred to as antigen D. Blood from people with the D antigen (Rh$^+$) is agglutinated by anti-D antibodies, which may be found in the blood of people without the antigen (Rh$^-$). Agglutination reactions that identify Rhesus blood types are shown in Table 2.

Table 2

Rhesus Blood Type	Anti-D Reaction (+/−)
Rh$^+$	+
Rh$^-$	−

Everyday Materials

❏ 10% bleach solution
❏ paper towels

Lab Materials

❏ ABO/Rh blood-typing test kit (with artificial or aseptic blood samples)

❏ protective gloves

Safety

- In this lab, you will work with artificial or aseptic blood samples obtained from your teacher. Handle and dispose of the samples as instructed by the testing kit or your teacher.

- Be sure to keep your hands away from your eyes and face in the science lab.

- Remember to wash your hands thoroughly before and after completing the lab procedure.

Procedure

1. Obtain an ABO/Rh blood-typing test kit from your teacher. Open the kit and assemble the contents for the procedure. Read the kit's instructions.

2. Obtain the blood sample from your teacher. Perform the ABO/Rh test as instructed by the kit. Pay close attention to the amount of time you need to wait for the samples to react.

3. After waiting the time specified in the kit instructions, observe the samples and compare them with **Figure 1**. Record the results, positive or negative for each reaction, in columns 1–3 of **Table 3** under *Data and Observations*.

4. Refer to **Tables 1** and **2** to determine ABO and Rh blood types based on the agglutination reactions. Record the ABO and Rh blood types in column 4 of **Table 3**. Notify your teacher of your results.

Cleanup and Disposal

1. Dispose of anything with blood on it immediately after use, according to your teacher's instructions.

2. Wipe down your work surface with the bleach solution and paper towels.

Lab 9 Use Blood Types to Help Solve a Crime, continued

Data and Observations
Table 3

1 Anti-A Reaction (+/−)	2 Anti-B Reaction (+/−)	3 Anti-D Reaction (+/−)	4 ABO/Rh Blood Type

Conclude and Apply

1. Your teacher will tell you the number of suspects of each blood type. The type of blood found at the crime scene is A+. Based on this information, how many suspects can be ruled out as possible perpetrators of the crime?

_____
_____
_____
_____
_____

2. Explain why blood types can be used only to rule out potential suspects and not to prove conclusively who committed a crime.

_____
_____
_____
_____

3. If you could test for other blood-group types in addition to ABO and Rh, how might this affect the investigation?

_____
_____
_____
_____

Analyze and Conclude

4. All of the ABO/Rh blood types are relatively common in the United States. The most common, O⁺,
   occurs in 38 percent of people; the least common, AB⁻, occurs in 1 percent of people. A⁺, which was
   found at the crime scene, occurs in 34 percent of people. Some blood-group systems do not show as
   much variation, and only a small percentage of people do not have the same blood type. How useful
   would a less variable blood-group system be for forensic analysis?

   _____

   _____

   _____

   _____

   _____

   _____

   _____

   _____

   _____

Lab 10 The Missing Restaurant Owner

The Problem

The following is a description of a fictitious murder case. The victim is a restaurant owner who was last known to be at a bus stop approximately 800 meters from his home. He vanished and was never seen again.

Witnesses testified that they heard yelling from the office of the victim's restaurant about the time the victim usually left work for home. Using this testimony, police established the identity of the man the victim was arguing with, and they questioned him as a suspect. The suspect had scratches on his face, which he claimed were from a fight he had the previous evening, and soil particles in his ring and bracelet. The suspect had no explanation for the soil particles or for the reports of yelling from the restaurant office. After arresting the suspect, the police searched his car, the restaurant office, and the surrounding countryside and gathered the following evidence:

List of Evidence

From the suspect's car (trunk):

- Bloodstained watch with the clasp missing (identified as the victim's)
- Strands of hair

From the restaurant office:

- Clasp matching the watch from the suspect's trunk
- Blood samples from the floor

Countryside:

- Bloodstained clothes wrapped in trash bags similar to those used by the restaurant; samples of hair from one of the suspect's dogs and thread from the suspect's sweater found on the clothes
- Knotted electrical cord with hairs that matched those found in the suspect's trunk

The hairs found in the car and on the electrical cord matched samples of the victim's hair taken from his home. Neither the murder weapon nor the body have been found. Your job is to evaluate the forensics evidence and come to a decision about the guilt or innocence of the suspect.

Lab 10 **The Missing Restaurant Owner,** *continued*

Part 1

Blood Type Analysis This case is peculiar because there is no body, only hair samples and bloodstains. Whose blood was found? The first thing to do is type the blood samples and then try to identify them.

Three genes (i^A, i^B, i) determine human blood type. Two genes (i^A and i^B) code for two proteins, A and B, that are found on the surface of red blood cells. The i gene does not code for a protein. Because you inherit one gene from your mother and one from your father, there are several possible genotypes and phenotypes (i.e. blood types). If you have one copy of i^A ($i^A i^A$ or $i^A i$), then your red blood cells will have the A protein (blood type A). If you have one copy of i^B ($i^B i^B$ or $i^B i$), then your cells will

express the B protein (type B). If you have a copy of i^A and i^B ($i^A i^B$), then your cells will express both proteins (type AB). If you only have i genes (ii), then your blood cells will express no protein (type O).

Blood typing is a fast, inexpensive, and easy procedure. To determine blood type, two drops or samples of blood are placed side by side on a glass slide. To one side, a drop of an antibody (anti-A) raised against the A protein is added, while to the other side, a drop of an antibody (anti-B) raised against the B protein is added. If A protein is present on the blood cells, then anti-A will cause them to clump together; likewise anti-B will cause the cells to clump if B protein is present. If no clumping is observed, then neither protein is present.

Procedure

1. Blood type slides from several of the pieces of bloodstained evidence are shown below (anti-A is on the left side and anti-B is on the right side of each slide). The blood-type slide from the suspect is also shown. Because police did not have a blood type for the missing restaurant owner, blood samples were drawn from his parents and are shown as well. Analyze the slides and determine all of the blood types.

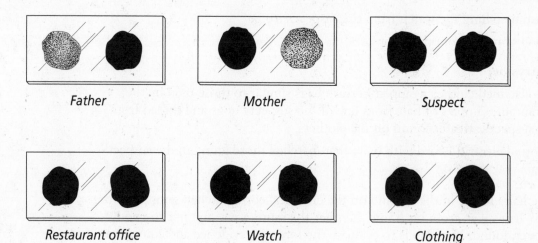

Father   Mother   Suspect

Restaurant office   Watch   Clothing

Blood Types:

Father _____   Mother _____   Suspect _____

Clothing _____   Restaurant office _____   Watch _____

Analyze and Conclude

2. Is it possible that the blood found in the office and on the clothing was the missing restaurant owner's blood? What was his blood type? Use your knowledge of genetic crosses (i.e., Punnett squares) to determine the victim's possible blood types from the information that you have. Show your work in the space below.

_____

_____

_____

_____

Part 2

DNA-Typing Analysis The blood-typing evidence did not clearly reveal whether the bloodstains belonged to the missing victim. So, investigators turned to a newer technique called DNA fingerprinting or DNA typing. The DNA sequence of human genes (DNA that codes for proteins) follows fairly regular patterns; however, the DNA sequences between genes (i.e. non-coding DNA) differ greatly among individuals. Scientists understand how to identify and analyze these special sequences, so they can tell if two DNA samples probably came from the same person. Since DNA is inherited from each parent, an individual shares patterns within these sequences with his or her parents. Therefore, scientists can also tell whether or not two samples came from individuals who are related.

To conduct a DNA typing experiment, traces of DNA are collected from an individual or crime scene. Then, a technique called polymerase chain reaction (PCR) is used to make copies of the DNA to increase the amount. PCR enables analyzable DNA to be obtained from extremely small samples. The DNA is then cut into fragments using specific enzymes called restriction enzymes.

The fragments, which are of different sizes, are separated using a technique called gel electrophoresis. The pattern of separated DNA fragments are transferred from the gel to a piece of filter paper and mixed with radioactive segments of DNA that correspond to an individual's unique sequences. After exposing the filter paper to the radioactive compounds, it is dried and exposed to X-ray film; the fragments containing an individual's unique sequences will show up as dark bands on the film. Now you have a DNA fingerprint. In practice, many DNA samples are loaded on the gel for comparison.

DNA typing compares the bands from a known sample to those of suspects. The bands from two different samples will match only if the same individual donated both samples. Even though an individual's pattern of bands is unique, children will share bands with both parents.

To verify the identity of the victim, DNA typing was done using samples of DNA from his mother (A), father (B), the suspect (C), the watch (D), the restaurant office (E), and the clothing (F). Read the gels on the next page from top to bottom and compare the columns.

Lab 10 The Missing Restaurant Owner, continued

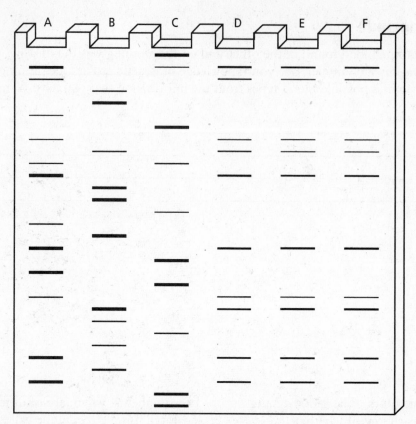

3. Was the victim genetically related to the mother and father tested in columns A and B? Explain your answer.

_____

_____

_____

4. Given that there was no body or murder weapon found, do you think that the evidence indicates beyond a reasonable doubt that the suspect murdered the victim? Explain your answer.

_____

_____

_____

Analyze and Conclude

5. Form groups of four students. Two students should act as prosecutors while the other two act as defense attorneys. Each pair should prepare an argument explaining why the suspect is guilty (prosecution) or innocent (defense). Use the lines below to list ideas you will use in your argument.

_____

_____

_____

Purpose

In this activity, students will learn about diffusion and osmosis and apply this knowledge to determine where two bodies found in a bay drowned and determine whether they were the victims of accidental drowning or murder.

Biological Concepts

Have students review the following concepts before beginning this activity:
❏ diffusion
❏ osmosis
❏ selected permeabilty

Time

1 hour

Teaching Tips

- This activity should be done with groups of three students.
- Sugar from the grocery store is cheaper and can be used in place of lab-grade sucrose.

Background

The students place 10% sucrose in dialysis bags and place the bags in various solutions [1% (A), 5% (B), 10% (C), 20% (D), and 40% (E)]. Note that Beakers A–E are set up to give students practice understanding osmosis and osmotic pressure. Beakers F and G represent the circumstances of the drowning victims, with the solutions inside the bags representing the water in the lungs (fresh or salt), and the solutions in the beakers representing the victims' blood. Students should measure the changes in weight of the bags after 30 minutes. Solutions in Beakers A and B are hypotonic relative to the bags, so water will flow from the solutions into the bags and increase the weights of Bags A and B (A > B). Beaker C is isotonic relative to the bag, so flow across the membrane should be equal in both directions and there should be no significant change in the weight of Bag C. Beakers D and E are hypertonic relative to

the bags, so water should flow from the bags into the solutions and decrease the weights of Bags D and E (D < E).

Beaker F represents a victim who drowned in freshwater, as explained in the lab. The 1% sucrose in the bag is hypotonic relative to the 10% solution in the beaker. Water should flow from the bag into the beaker, and the bag will lose weight. Consequently, the concentration of sucrose in the bag will increase, and the concentration of sucrose in the beaker (blood) should decrease. In contrast, Beaker G represents a victim who drowned in salt water, as explained in the lab. The 40% sucrose in the bag is hypertonic relative to the 10% solution in the beaker. Water should flow from the beaker into the bag and the bag will gain weight. Consequently, the concentration of sucrose in the bag will decrease, and the concentration of sucrose in the beaker (blood) should increase.

Students will use the hypothetical blood concentration data of the drowning victims to determine whether the victims drowned in freshwater or salt water. The concentrations of sodium, potassium, and chloride increased in the man's blood, which indicates that he drowned in salt water. In contrast, the concentrations of these ions decreased in the woman's blood, which indicates that she drowned in freshwater. Encourage students to discuss different ways a victim who drowned in freshwater could end up in salt water and to discuss any other evidence that might help determine whether the deaths were murders or accidents.

Advance Preparation

1. On the day before the lab, cut the dialysis tubing into sections and soak in water.
2. On the day before the lab, prepare the sucrose solutions. You can refrigerate the solutions overnight, but warm them to room

Sucrose Concentration %	40% Sucrose (mL)	Water (mL)	Total (mL)
10	1000	3000	4000
1	50	1950	2000
5	250	1750	2000
20	1000	1000	2000

temperature prior to use. Make 4.3 L of 40% sucrose stock solution by dissolving 1.72 kg sucrose in 4.3 L of water. Make dilutions of the stock solution to yield the following sucrose solutions in the table below:

Answers

1. The masses of Bags A and B should increase. The mass gain of Bag A should be greater than that of Bag B.

2. The concentrations of Beakers A and B were less than the concentrations inside the bags. You would classify them as hypotonic relative to the bags.

3. The concentrations of sucrose inside Bags A and B were greater than the surrounding solutions. Therefore, the water concentrations inside the bags were less than those in the surrounding solutions. Water diffused from the beakers (high concentration) into the bags (low concentration), thereby increasing the masses of the bags. The difference in the water concentration across the bag was greater in Bag A than in Bag B. Therefore, Bag A had more water diffuse into it and showed a greater mass gain than Bag B.

4. The mass of Bag C should not change.

5. The concentration of sucrose inside Bag C was the same as the concentration of sucrose in the beaker. Therefore, Bag C was isotonic compared to the surrounding solution.

6. Because the concentrations of sucrose inside and outside Bag C were the same, there was no difference in the concentration of water across the bag. Therefore, the diffusion of water across the membrane was equal in both directions, and the mass of Bag C did not change.

7. The masses of Bags D and E should decrease. The mass loss of Bag E should be greater than that of Bag D.

8. The concentrations of Beakers D and E were greater than the concentrations inside the bags. You would classify them as hypertonic relative to the bags.

9. The concentrations of sucrose inside Bags D and E were less than the surrounding solutions. Therefore, the water concentrations inside the bags were greater than those in the surrounding solutions. Water diffused from the bags (high concentration) into the beakers (low concentration), thereby decreasing the masses of the bags. The difference in the water concentration across the bag was greater in Bag E than in Bag D. Therefore, Bag E had more water diffuse out of it and showed a greater loss of mass than Bag D.

10. The bag should lose mass, which indicates that water moved out of the bag. The concentration of sucrose in the beaker, which represents the salts in the blood, was greater than inside the bag, which represents the salt concentration in the freshwater in the lungs; therefore, the concentration of water inside the bag was greater than the surrounding solution. Water diffused out of the bag and diluted the contents of the surrounding solution. So, the concentration of sucrose in the beaker should decrease.

11. The bag should gain weight, which indicates that water moved into the bag. The concentration of sucrose in the beaker, which represents the salts in the blood, was less than inside the bag, which represents the salt concentration in the salt water in the lungs; therefore, the concentration of water inside the bag was less than the surrounding solution. Water diffused into the bag. The loss of water from the beaker solution increased the sucrose concentration in the beaker.

12. The increased salt concentration of the man's blood indicated that he drowned in salt water, possibly the San Francisco Bay, much like the situation in Beaker G. In contrast, the salt concentration in the woman's blood indicated that she drowned in freshwater, much like the situation in Beaker F.

13. Because the data indicate that the man drowned in salt water, it is possible that he drowned in the San Francisco Bay and that his death could have been an accident. Other evidence would be needed to determine that his death was not an accident. Because the data indicate that the woman drowned in freshwater, it seems likely that the woman was drowned elsewhere and her body was dumped into the bay as a result of a murder; however, you might also conclude that she drowned in a river or freshwater tributary of the bay and was washed into the San Francisco Bay prior to her discovery.

Lab 2 How can you extract DNA from cells?

Purpose

The purpose of this lab is to demonstrate DNA extraction and the role it plays in genetic engineering. For example, genetic engineers need to extract DNA in order to isolate a beneficial gene. They might then take the gene from the extracted DNA, insert it into bacteria cells, and use the bacteria to make many copies of the gene.

Biological Concepts

Have students review the following concepts before beginning this activity:

❏ genetic engineering

❏ DNA extraction

❏ membrane structure

❏ biomolecules, such as lipids and proteins

Expected Outcome

Students should be able to extract DNA from banana cells and observe as it precipitates out of alcohol.

Time

1 hour

Advance Preparation

- Prepare a test tube containing 95% ethanol or 91% isopropyl alcohol for each student. Seal the tubes with stoppers and keep the test tubes on ice until they are needed. The colder the alcohol, the better the results.

- If you do not have enough pipettes, students can use droppers instead.

- To avoid long waits to use the blender, you can prepare the banana and water mixture just before class begins. Make enough so that each student has approximately 3 heaping teaspoons of the mixture.

Teaching Strategies

- Introduce the lab by asking students what they would change about bananas to make them a more appealing food. (Possible answers might include to make them more flavorful or less easily bruised.)

- Point out that genetically changing a food, such as the banana, requires alteration of its DNA. Briefly review one or more specific genetic engineering procedures for altering DNA, such as the cutting and pasting techniques used for making recombinant DNA.

Teaching Tips

- If access to a blender is limited, have students make their own banana and water mixture by mashing those ingredients in a sealed plastic bag.

- Remind students not to shake or stir the test tube in Step 6 of the Procedure.

- The DNA that precipitates out in Step 7 will have the appearance of white, stringy mucus. When good results are obtained, there will be enough DNA to spool onto a glass rod or wooden coffee stirrer. To spool the DNA, carefully dip the stick into the part of the tube where the DNA is forming. Gently twirl the stick between your thumb and forefinger; the stringy DNA will spool onto the stick. If the tip of a Pasteur pipetette is heated and formed into a hook, students may be able to use it to retrieve some of the DNA from the alcohol layer.

Answers

1. The role of the shampoo is to dissolve the fats and proteins that make up the cell membrane and to form complexes with them so they can be filtered out of solution.

2. The DNA would not precipitate out of water as it does out of alcohol in Step 7 of the *Procedure* because DNA is soluble in water.

3. You could not use DNA extracted from cooked food because the heat would denature the DNA.

4. DNA extraction is the first step because genetic engineering procedures involve manipulation of DNA molecules.

Lab 3

How can you transform cells with new DNA?

Purpose

The purpose of this lab is to give students hands-on experience with genetic engineering and an understanding of how genetic engineering can be used in fighting human diseases.

Biological Concepts

Have students review the following concepts before beginning this activity:
❑ DNA transformation
❑ gene therapy
❑ genetic disorders
❑ bacteria

Expected Outcome

Students should be able to transform *E. coli* with plasmid DNA to produce bacteria that glow and are antibiotic resistant.

Time

1 hour the first day; 10 minutes 2 days later

Instructor's Materials List

❑ nonpathogenic strain of *E. coli*
❑ Qiagen Maxi-prep purified plasmid DNA (pLux)
❑ Luria broth
❑ 100 mg/mL ampicillin
❑ culture plates/petri dishes
❑ bactotryptone
❑ bacto-yeast extract
❑ NaCl
❑ KCl
❑ $5M$ NaOH
❑ autoclave
❑ $CaCl_2$
❑ $MnCl_2$
❑ $MgCl_2$
❑ glycerol
❑ HCl
❑ bacto-agar
❑ flasks
❑ centrifuge
❑ liquid nitrogen or dry-ice ethanol bath

Advance Preparation

• **CAUTION:** Any students with a compromised immune system should not participate in the lab.

• Be sure to read the MSDS information for each chemical you are using.

• From a biological supply company, order a nonpathogenic strain of *E. coli*, Qiagen Maxi-Prep purified plasmid DNA (pLux), Luria broth, and 100 mg/mL ampicillin (1 mL). Check that other needed supplies are in stock.

• At least 2 days before the lab, prepare medium, buffer, plasmid, and agar plates.

• For medium: use 20 g bactotryptone, 5 g bacto-yeast extract, 0.5 g NaCl, 0.2 g KCl, H_2O to bring total volume to 1 L; adjust pH to 7.0 with $5M$ NaOH; autoclave for 20 minutes.

• For buffer: use 11.8 g $CaCl_2$, 4.0 g $MnCl_2$, 2.0 g $MgCl_2$, 0.7 g KCl, 100 mL glycerol; adjust pH to 6.4 with HCl; add H_2O to bring total volume to 1 L; filter sterilize.

• For plasmid: use Qiagen Maxi-Preps for plasmid purification, yielding a plasmid stock of 1 mg plasmid DNA/mL; dilute to 100 ng/5 μL; store at –20°C until needed. It is very important that the pH is correct for these bacteria.

• For agar plates: use 10 g bactotryptone, 5 g bacto-yeast extract, 10 g NaCl, H_2O to bring volume to 1 L; add 15 g bacto-agar; autoclave 20 minutes; cool to about 55°C; add 1 mL of 100 mg/mL ampicillin; filter sterilize; mix; pour about 15 mL into each petri dish; let sit overnight to harden.

• At least 1 day before the lab, grow an overnight culture of *E. coli* in 2-mL medium; transfer to flask; add 125 mL medium; incubate at 37°C for 2 hours with shaking; place on ice 10 minutes; centrifuge; remove supernatant; resuspend cell pellet in 40-mL cold buffer;

incubate on ice 20 minutes; centrifuge; remove supernatant; resuspend cell pellet in 10-mL cold buffer; aliquot cells into 100-μL volumes; quick freeze in liquid nitrogen or dry-ice ethanol bath; store at –80°C until 1 hour before use, then thaw cells on ice.

Teaching Strategy

- Explain that the Lux gene in the plasmid DNA has been isolated from another species of glowing bacteria and will cause the transformed *E. coli* to glow. A similar gene is found in fireflies. The plasmid also contains a gene that is resistant to ampicillin.

Teaching Tips

- Divide the class into groups. The materials listed on the student page are the amounts needed by one group. Groups should do Parts A and B at the same time by dividing the work among members.

- For students to see the cells glowing, they will need to be in an extremely dark environment.

- In Step 18, reasonable hypotheses include: bacteria will grow only on the LUX plate; bacteria growing on the LUX plate will glow.

- Dispose of all chemicals and reagents as instructed by the manufacturer and by local, state, and national guidelines.

Answers

1. There are bacteria on the LUX plate due to the plasmid gene for ampicillin resistance. Because of the Lux gene in the plasmid DNA, bacteria on the LUX plate glow.

2. The control culture shows that *E. coli* does not normally have resistance to ampicillin or the ability to glow.

3. Ampicillin was used to detect the plasmid DNA marker gene for antibiotic resistance. Ampicillin also ensures that only transformed cells will multiply, which is important because the transformed cells also contain the Lux gene.

4. Genetic engineering might be used to transform nonfunctioning, insulin-producing cells with a new gene for insulin production. This would allow the cells to produce insulin.

How can you transcribe and translate a gene?

Purpose

The purpose of this lab is to demonstrate how the genetic code is used in protein synthesis and the role a universal genetic code plays in biotechnology.

Biological Concepts

Have students review the following concepts before beginning this activity:
❏ transcription and translation of genes
❏ point mutations

Expected Outcome

Students should be able to use the genetic code to identify amino acid sequences encoded by DNA sequences and identify which DNA sequence codes for part of a human hemoglobin molecule.

Time

45 minutes

Teaching Strategies

- Introduce the lab by reviewing the building blocks of DNA and proteins.

- Call on students to explain or illustrate DNA base complementarity. Clarify any misconceptions.

Teaching Tips

- To save class time, you can assign each student just one of the two mystery DNA sequences to transcribe and translate, but make sure that both are decoded.

- Explain to the class how to read the genetic code in the table. Point out the letters heading the four main rows. Tell students that these letters represent the first base in each codon in the table. The second base is represented by the letters heading the four columns. Thus, the first two letters place each codon in a particular cell in the table. The other codons in the cell differ only in the third base, with all four bases being represented in each cell. Call on students at random to read amino acids encoded by different codons in the table to check their understanding.

Answers

1. The sequences of amino acids for the mystery DNA sequences are: #1, Met Val His Leu Thr Pro Glu Gly Lys; and #2, Met Val Leu Thr Pro Gly Glu His Lys. The sequences of the first nine amino acids for the four human hemoglobins are: normal Hb, Met Val His Leu Thr Pro Glu Glu Lys; Hb S, Met Val His Leu Thr Pro Val Glu Lys; Hb C, Met Val His Leu Thr Pro Lys Glu Lys; and Hb G, Met Val His Leu Thr Pro Glu Gly Lys. The amino acid sequence for mystery DNA sequence #1 matches the amino acid sequence of hemoglobin G.

2. For hemoglobin S, the codon in position seven, CTC, which codes for glutamic acid, mutates to become CAC, which codes for valine. For hemoglobin C, the codon in position seven mutates to become TTC, which codes for lysine. For hemoglobin G, the codon in position eight, CTC, which codes for glutamic acid, mutates to become CCC, which codes for glycine.

3. No, because both CTC and CTT code for glutamic acid.

4. It would cause premature termination of protein synthesis because ATC codes for a "stop" codon. As a result, only incomplete copies of the protein would be synthesized.

5. Because it is consistent between organisms, the genetic code for human proteins can be transcribed and translated by genetically engineered bacteria to produce large amounts of vital human proteins that cannot be synthesized outside of living cells.

Lab 5 How can you diagnose genotypes using DNA?

Purpose

The purpose of this lab is to simulate the diagnosis of sickle-cell genotypes with DNA restriction enzyme analysis.

Biological Concepts

Have students review the following concepts before beginning this activity:

❏ genetically related diseases

❏ inheritance

❏ mutations

❏ gel electrophoresis

Expected Outcome

Students should be able to determine the genotypes of family members and the chance of the parents having a child with sickle-cell anemia.

Time

45 minutes

Advance Preparation

- To make the dye mixtures, dissolve 0.025 g xylene cyanole (XC) or napthol blue (NB) in 10 mL water and 1 mL glycerol.

DNA Samples			
Individual	Label	Family #1	Family #2
Mother	M	Carrier (XC+NB)	Carrier (XC+NB)
Father	F	Carrier (XC+NB)	Normal (NB)
Teenager	T	Carrier (XC+NB)	Normal (NB)
Infant	I	Sickle-cell (XC)	Carrier (XC+NB)
Known Normal	N	Normal (NB)	Normal (NB)
Known Carrier	C	Carrier (XC+NB)	Carrier (XC+NB)
Known Sickle-Cell	S	Sickle-cell (XC)	Sickle-cell (XC)

- Prepare 7 dye ("DNA") samples for each group of students. Half the groups should be given samples that represent Family #1 and the other half given samples that represent Family #2. Prepare the samples according to the table. For the carrier samples, use equal parts of each dye solution. Label the test tubes with the appropriate letters.

- Prepare and pour the gels ahead of time so they will be ready to use by the start of class. Tape both ends of a 1% agarose gel cassette and place a well-forming comb in the slot. Pour one bottle of premelted agarose into the cassette, filling it almost completely. Let the agarose solidify, and then carefully remove the tape and comb.

Teaching Strategies

- Explain that napthol blue and xylene cyanole are dyes that look similar but move at different rates through gel during electrophoresis, so that two distinct bands are produced. Both dyes are negatively charged and thus, run toward the red electrode, or the positively charged end of the gel, as does DNA.

- Point out that, in this lab, napthol blue represents DNA fragments with the A allele because it mimics the smaller-fragment band of normal DNA; xylene cyanole represents DNA fragments with the S allele because it mimics the larger-fragment band of DNA with the sickle-cell mutation; and a 1:1 mixture of the two dyes represents DNA fragments with both A and S alleles because it mimics the smaller- and larger-fragment bands of DNA.

- Call on students to explain the purpose of the three known DNA samples in their analysis. Clarify any misunderstandings.

Teaching Tips

- Divide the class into groups of up to seven students each for this lab. Have each student answer the questions.

- The dyes will diffuse quickly through the gel, so advise students to record their results as soon as possible after running the gel.

Answers

1. The two dyes look alike, but move at different rates through the gel during electrophoresis. This occurs so that two distinct bands can be seen, similar to the bands of DNA fragments of different lengths. The dyes also are negatively charged and move toward the positive end of the gel, as does DNA.

2. For Family #1, genotypes are: mother, AS; father, AS; teenager, AS; infant, SS. For Family #2, genotypes are: mother, AS; father, AA; teenager, AA; infant, AS.

3. For Family #1, the chance of having a child with sickle-cell anemia is 25%. For Family #2, the chance is zero.

4. If the enzyme cut the DNA at another nucleotide sequence, it could not be used to diagnose sickle-cell genotypes. The mutation causing the disease would no longer affect the enzyme's ability to recognize and cut DNA. Thus, the resulting DNA fragments would be the same length as, and indistinguishable from, normal DNA fragments.

Lab 6

How can genetically engineered plants be multiplied?

Purpose

The purpose of this lab is to demonstrate the technique of micropropagation and the role it plays in environmental biotechnology. As plants are genetically engineered to be more disease resistant or to produce larger, tastier fruits, specialized biotechnological techniques such as micropropagation must be carefully carried out. Such techniques have led to great success in creating improved plants.

Biological Concepts

Have students review the following concepts before beginning this activity:
❑ DNA transfer
❑ micropropogation

Expected Outcome

Students should be able to culture African violet shoots from pieces of disinfected leaves using a sterile growing medium and aseptic conditions.

Time

1 hour the first day; 5 minutes once a week for the next 5 weeks

Instructor's Materials List

❑ African violet medium
❑ liquid dish detergent
❑ distilled water
❑ bleach
❑ glass jars with lids
❑ sugar
❑ agar
❑ aluminum foil
❑ NaOH
❑ HCl

Advance Preparation

- Be sure to read the MSDS information for any chemical you are using.

- You can obtain prepackaged African violet medium from a biological supply company.

- Prepare the 0.1% detergent solution by adding 1 mL of liquid dishwashing detergent to 1 liter of distilled water. Prepare the 10% bleach solution by adding 100 mL of household bleach to 1 liter of distilled water.

- Sterile water for the rinses can be prepared by placing loosely capped bottles or other glass containers of distilled water in a boiling water bath for 30 minutes. After cooling, keep the sterile water capped until ready to use.

- To save class time, you can prepare the culture medium in advance instead of having students prepare it. One liter of culture medium (enough for 16 students) can be prepared using an entire package of African violet medium, 30 g of sugar, enough distilled water to bring the solution up to 1 liter, and 8.0 g of agar. Prepare the solution following the directions provided in Part B of the *Procedure*.

- Sterilize razor blades and forceps by wrapping them in aluminum foil and baking them in a conventional oven at 350°F for 15 minutes.

- Provide 1.0 and 0.1 molar solutions of NaOH and HCl for students to use in adjusting the pH of the medium. To obtain a 0.1 molar solution, you can dilute the 1.0 molar solution with distilled water (for example, 1 mL of a 1.0 molar solution diluted with 9 mL of distilled water to a volume of 10 mL).

Teaching Strategies

- Demonstrate how a plant can be propagated asexually using a stem cutting. Explain why this method cannot be used to propagate small amounts of genetically engineered plant tissue.

- Be sure the investigation is carried out in a well-ventilated room. Fumes may be hazardous to students with breathing difficulties such as asthma.

Teaching Tips

- Divide the class into pairs to work on the lab. Have one partner prepare the culture medium (Part B) while the other partner disinfects the leaves (Part C).

- Provide students with an undisturbed place to keep their cultures under fluorescent lights and out of direct sunlight for 16 hours a day at about 25°C.

- If a sterile environment was not maintained, contamination will be apparent within a few days. Make sure any contaminated petri dishes are discarded promptly.

- Shoots should start growing in about two weeks and be visible with the unaided eye in five weeks.

Answers

1. It is crucial to maintain aseptic conditions to avoid contamination of the culture medium. If aseptic conditions are not maintained, bacteria or fungi are likely to contaminate and take over the medium and infect the plant tissues.

2. Plant micropropagation allows genetic engineers to propagate large numbers of genetically identical plants from tiny pieces of genetically altered tissue. Other propagation techniques are slower and require much larger pieces of plant material.

3. It is possible because each cell of a plant holds all the DNA of the organism and, thus, can lead to the development of an entire plant.

4. Using micropropagation, breeders and growers can propagate plants asexually to produce millions of new plants from a single plant. This allows them to introduce new cultivars far sooner than if they were using conventional propagation techniques.

Lab 7 — When did she die?

Purpose

In this activity, students will play the role of a medical examiner and use various biological data (e.g. body temperature, rigor mortis, livor mortis, eye appearance, stomach contents) to determine the time of death of a victim.

Biological Concepts

Have students review the following concepts before beginning this activity:
- ❏ human physiology
- ❏ pathology
- ❏ ATP in muscle contractions
- ❏ digestion

Expected Outcome

Students will examine crime scene and autopsy evidence to determine when the victim died.

Time

30–45 minutes

Teaching Tips

- The activity can be done individually or in groups of two.
- You might want to entertain a debate or discussion about the circumstances surrounding the death.
- You may wish to bring in a medical examiner or a member of a police forensics team to discuss his/her job with the students and the use of biology in crime-solving.
- Students could use a final report format similar to a medical examiner's report instead of the traditional questions and answers.

Background

The victim was found lying facedown at the bottom of the stairs in her townhouse. From the temperature of her body (27°C), students will be able to estimate that she died 11.5 hours before, or at 11:00 P.M., the previous night. Her body was in complete rigor mortis, which is consistent with the estimated time of death from body temperature measurements. Her body showed fixed lividity on the shoulders and neck; these marks were not inconsistent with a fall down the stairs. Her stomach was empty, but her small intestine had food in it, which indicates that she died at least 4–6 hours after eating. This finding is consistent with the 5:00 P.M. dinner with her sister. Her eyes were cloudy, which indicates that death occured at least 2–3 hours before.

Students might speculate that the victim died at approximately 11:00 P.M. the night before. She must have eaten dinner at least 4–6 hours before death. She died of a broken neck and the scene might suggest that it was an accidental death when she fell down the steps after returning home late Friday evening.

Answers

1. The normal body temperature is 37°C.

2. The breakdown of foods (i.e. metabolism) provides the heat energy necessary for humans, mammals, and birds to maintain their body temperatures above the temperature of their surroundings.

3. To contract, the myosin filaments form chemical bonds called crossbridges. These crossbridges are repeatedly formed and broken as a muscle contracts. ATP is required to break the crossbridges. When ATP is no longer present (i.e. after death), the crossbridges form and muscles contract, but cannot relax. Within about 24–48 hours, the proteins in the muscles begin to decompose and the effects of rigor mortis lessen.

4. Food enters your body through your mouth and, when you swallow, continues down your esophagus into your stomach. After the food is digested in your stomach, it proceeds into the small intestine where most of the nutrients are absorbed. From the small intestine, the food passes into the large intestine where water is absorbed and feces are formed and stored in the rectum. The feces leave the rectum through the anus.

5.

Hour	Body Temp. (°C)	Hour	Body Temp. (°C)	Hour	Body Temp. (°C)
1	36.2	9	29.5	17	24.9
2	35.3	10	28.7	18	24.5
3	34.5	11	27.8	19	24.1
4	33.7	12	27	20	23.7
5	32.8	13	26.6	21	23.3
6	32	14	26.2	22	22.8
7	31.2	15	25.8	23	22.4
8	30.3	16	25.3	24	22

6.

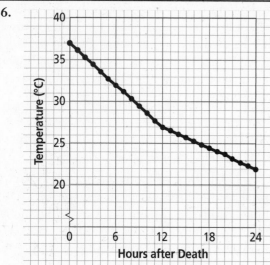

7. The victim's body temperature was 27°C, which would indicate that she had been dead approximately 11.5 hours.

8. Since her body temperature was measured at 10:30 A.M., she probably died approximately 11:00 P.M. the previous night.

9. Because the body was in complete rigor mortis, which takes approximately 8–12 hours, the victim must have been dead at least 8–12 hours but less than 24–48 hours, the time frame in which the body relaxes again.

10. Lividity was observed on the front of her shoulders and neck and was fixed. Because lividity was fixed, she must have been dead at least 6–8 hours. The victim was found lying face down, so the lividity marks are consistent with the position in which the body was found.

11. The victim must have died with her eyes open because they were cloudy and a thin film had developed. She must have been dead at least 2–3 hours.

12. It takes approximately 4–6 hours for the stomach to empty into the small intestine. The victim's stomach was empty, but her small intestine contained food, which indicates that she must have died at least 4–6 hours after she had eaten her last meal.

13. The victim was found lying facedown at the bottom of the stairs in her townhouse. From the temperature of her body (27°C), she died 11.5 hours before, or at approximately 11:00 P.M., the previous night. Her body was in complete rigor mortis, which is consistent with the estimated time of death from body temperature measurements because complete rigor mortis occurs 8–12 hours after death. Her stomach was empty, but her small intestine had food in it, which indicates that she died at least 4–6 hours after eating. Her eyes were cloudy, which indicates that death occurred at least 2–3 hours before. In all, the evidence is consistent with an estimate of 11:00 P.M. for time of death.

14. The victim died at approximately 11:00 P.M. the night before. The scene suggests that it was an accidental death when she fell down the steps after returning home late Friday evening. The death is probably accidental.

Lab 8 A Sweet Season

Purpose

In this activity, students will measure glucose in simulated plasma samples, plot data for a glucose tolerance test, diagnose two hypothetical patients for possible diabetes, and learn about diabetes and glucose metabolism.

Biological Concepts

Have students review the following concepts before beginning this activity:
- ❏ diabetes
- ❏ digestive system
- ❏ glucose in the bloodstream
- ❏ insulin

Expected Outcome

Students will simulate a blood glucose test and diagnose diabetes in the patients.

Time

30–45 minutes

Instructor's Materials List

- ❏ glucose solutions made from glucose tablets (5 g per tablet, Becton-Dickinson, available from local pharmacy)
- ❏ distilled water
- ❏ four reagent bottles with caps (500 mL)
- ❏ Diastix™ Reagent test strips for Urinalysis (Bayer Corporation, available from local pharmacy), 12 per group
- ❏ plastic or glass test tubes with caps (5–10 mL capacity)
- ❏ test-tube rack, one per group
- ❏ stopwatch or other watch with a second hand, one per group
- ❏ tissues to wipe excess fluid
- ❏ ruler, one per student

Advance Preparation

(for a class of 30 students, 15 groups of 2)

1. Make 1 L of 1000 mg/dL (10 g/L) stock solution by dissolving 2 glucose tablets in 1 L of distilled water. Label this solution A. You will have more of this solution than you need.

2. Make 500 mL of each glucose solution from the stock solution as follows:

   Solution B: 100 mg/dL (1 g/L) = 50 mL of stock + 450 mL of water

   Solution C: 250 mg/dL (2.5 g/L) = 125 mL of stock + 375 mL of water

   Solution D: 500 mg/dL (5 g/L) = 250 mL of stock + 250 mL of water

3. For each group, label 12 tubes as follows: Jorge (0, 0.5, 1.0, 1.5, 2.0, 2.5) and Kyle (0, 0.5, 1.0, 1.5, 2.0, 2.5)

4. Pour 5 mL of the appropriate solution in the following tubes, cap each tube, and place in the racks.

Time (h)	Jorge	Kyle
0	B	C
0.5	C	D
1.0	B	A
1.5	B	A
2.0	B	D
2.5	B	D

5. The solutions should be made the morning of the lab or the day before and stored in a refrigerator overnight. If refrigerated, the solutions should be warmed to room temperature prior to use in the activity.

6. If possible, make color copies of the color scale from the Diastix™ bottle for each group. (Otherwise, a description of the color scale is provided in the activity.)

7. Give each group a copy of the insulin data after they have completed question 6.

Plasma Insulin Concentration (μU/mL)		
Time (h)	**Jorge**	**Kyle**
0	50	25
0.5	80	30
1.0	100	45
1.5	90	50
2.0	60	60
2.5	50	55

Background

When glucose is ingested, it passes through the esophagus and stomach into the small intestine, where it is absorbed into the portal vein. Glucose then passes through the portal vein into the liver prior to entering the general blood circulation. In the liver, glucose is stored as glycogen if insulin is present. The presence of glucose in the small intestine causes the pancreas to release insulin, which allows cells (i.e. liver, muscle, fat) to absorb glucose and causes these cells to store glucose in the form of glycogen and convert glucose to fatty acids. Thus, a spike of insulin precedes a small rise in blood glucose in normal individuals.

The oral glucose tolerance test (OGTT) is a common test for diabetes. To take the OGTT, a person fasts overnight and then drinks a solution containing glucose. Blood glucose levels are checked before drinking the solution and at regular intervals after drinking it. In a person who does not have diabetes (75-g OGTT), the initial reading should be between 60 and 110 mg/dL; after 1 hour the reading should be less than 200 mg/dL, and after 2 hours it should be less than 140 mg/dL. Elevated readings might indicate the person has diabetes.

Teaching Tip

Urine glucose tests are not as accurate as blood glucose tests; therefore, blood tests for glucose are greatly preferred. However, the urine may have to be tested for compounds called ketones. The presence of ketones in the urine can help distinguish between type 1 and type 2 diabetes; high levels of ketones can also mean the diabetic should seek the help of a doctor. Therefore, both blood and urine tests have important roles to play in monitoring diabetes.

Answers

1. Kyle's was higher:

   Jorge   100 mg/dL

   Kyle   250 mg/dL

2. Jorge's blood sugar increased from 100 mg/dL to 250 mg/dL within the first half hour and then returned to normal for the rest of the test. In contrast, Kyle's blood glucose started at 250 mg/dL and increased to 500 mg/dL within a half hour. Kyle's blood glucose took longer to decrease and had not returned to pretest levels by the end of the glucose tolerance test.

3. After passing through the mouth, esophagus, and stomach, glucose ends up in the small intestine, where it is absorbed. It passes across the walls of the small intestine into the hepatic portal vein, where it travels to the liver. Once in the liver, glucose is either stored as glycogen or released into the blood stream depending upon whether insulin is present or not. Shortly after a meal, there is a small increase in blood glucose as this process takes place.

4. Yes, for both boys, as mentioned above, glucose increases after a meal. However, because Kyle is diabetic, the changes in his blood glucose levels are exaggerated and the return toward his normal blood glucose level is slowed because he lacks insulin.

5. Jorge's blood glucose is more stable.

6. It appears that Kyle may have diabetes because (1) his pretest or fasting blood glucose level is higher and (2) the changes in his blood glucose levels during the test are exaggerated and uncontrolled.

7. As food (i.e. glucose) enters the small intestine, the pancreas begins to secrete insulin. Therefore, Jorge shows an increase in plasma insulin that peaks at one hour and slowly drops until the end of the test. In contrast, Kyle's insulin levels are low and increase slowly throughout the test (but they still remain below normal levels).

8. Plasma insulin in normal individuals increases about the same time that glucose levels begin to rise after the start of the test. They remain elevated throughout most of the test; the elevated insulin levels allow cells to absorb glucose and keep glucose levels near normal while it is absorbed. In the diabetic (Kyle), plasma insulin levels are below normal and rise slowly because Kyle's pancreas does not produce much insulin. This allows Kyle's blood glucose to remain elevated during the test.

9. Kyle has diabetes, probably type 1 because his insulin levels are low. He also exhibits symptoms of diabetes, such as constant hunger and thirst, weight loss, muscle weakness, and inability to withstand fasting between meals.

10. Insulin allows cells to absorb glucose, which lowers blood sugar and keeps it within normal limits after a meal.

11. Jorge will be able to withstand a long period without food because his blood glucose is well controlled. In contrast, Kyle shows wild fluctuations in blood glucose. Because Kyle lacks insulin, his cells cannot absorb and utilize glucose; therefore, his body feels that it is always starved.

12. Kyle does not have sufficient levels of insulin and proper insulin secretion in response to a meal. Therefore, his cells do not absorb and metabolize glucose. His body is in a "starved" state. So, Kyle's body signals him to eat constantly. Furthermore, his body breaks down muscle protein, which is why he feels weak. The elevated blood glucose causes his kidneys to excrete glucose, which also causes more water to be excreted for osmotic reasons. Therefore, Kyle urinates frequently and must drink to avoid dehydration. The elevated blood glucose causes him to feel sleepy, especially after a meal. Despite the increased appetite, Kyle cannot absorb glucose or benefit from the food that he eats; this condition along with the breakdown of muscle protein accounts for the weight loss.

13. Jorge's condition is probably caused by exhaustion from heavy physical activity. He needs rest. In contrast, Kyle has type 1 diabetes (insulin-dependent) and needs insulin treatment as well as proper diet and exercise. His blood glucose should be closely monitored.

Use Blood Types to Help Solve a Crime

Teacher Guide

Purpose

The purpose of this lab is to demonstrate a simple blood-typing procedure and the information blood types can provide to forensic investigations.

Biological Concepts

Have students review the following concepts before beginning this activity:
❑ antigen-antibody reactions
❑ blood types
❑ Rhesus blood types

Expected Outcome

Students should be able to determine ABO and Rhesus blood types using antigen-antibody agglutination reactions.

Time

45 minutes

Advance Preparation

- For realism, try to distribute the suspects' blood types roughly according to population parameters. For the U.S. population, these figures are O^+, 38%; O^-, 7%; A^+, 34%; A^-, 6%; B^+, 9%; B^-, 2%; AB^+, 3%; and AB^-, 1%. Assign these sample types to students before class, and record which type each student receives.

Teaching Strategies

- Introduce the lab by describing antigen-antibody reactions. Give students an analogy for how antigen-antibody complexes form, such as a lock and key or two jigsaw-puzzle pieces. Explain how the reactions result in the clumping together of red blood cells, which causes the red blood cells to separate out of the fluid portion of blood.

- Point out that blood typing can be quick and easy, as students will see when they do this lab. It can provide quick results before data from more expensive and time-consuming DNA tests are available. However, blood typing cannot conclusively identify an individual, as DNA analysis can.

- Be sure the investigation is carried out in a well-ventilated room. Fumes may be hazardous to students with breathing difficulties such as asthma.

Teaching Tips

- All used blood-typing cards and other materials possibly contaminated with blood should be promptly disposed of as biological hazardous waste. Follow proper precautions.

Answers

1. Students should rule out all suspects who do not have A^+ blood.

2. Too many people share the same blood type for blood type alone to prove conclusively who committed a crime.

3. The more blood groups you added, the more you could narrow down the list of potential perpetrators, at least to the extent that the additional blood types varied among suspects.

4. A less variable blood-group system would generally be less useful for forensic analysis because most people would have the same blood type.

Lab 10 — The Missing Restaurant Owner

Purpose

This activity is about the uses of forensic science in a murder case. The students play the role of forensic scientist and use blood typing data, genetic analysis, and DNA typing to identify the victim in the absence of a body or murder weapon. The activity fits well after discussions of genetics, blood grouping, and DNA technology.

Biological Concepts

Have students review the following concepts before beginning this activity:

❏ blood type analysis

❏ DNA analysis

Time

30–45 minutes

Teaching Strategies

- This activity can be done by individuals, in groups, or as a class discussion. Because the story builds section by section, it would be best to give the students one section at a time.

- The activity lends itself to debates on justice and the presence of physical evidence, and students must synthesize conclusions and opinions from several lines of evidence.

Answers

1. Blood Types:

Father	A
Mother	B
Suspect	O
Clothing	O
Restaurant office	O
Watch	O

2. Yes, it is possible that the blood found in the restaurant office and on the clothing belonged to the missing restaurant owner, even though the father was type A and the mother was type B. If both parents were heterozygotes, then their offspring would have the following possible blood types: A, B, AB, and O.

3. Yes. The blood on the watch, in the office, and on the clothing shares genetic elements (bands) with both the mother (A) and the father (B), but not with the suspect (C). This indicates that the blood on the evidence was not that of the suspect. Because it shares elements with the father and mother, the blood must have come from someone closely related to them.

4. The answer to this question is open to debate by students. The probability that the blood samples belong to the missing restaurant owner place him in the office where the crime allegedly took place. The blood samples and the strands of the victim's hair place him in the trunk of the suspect's car and in the countryside. The data would indicate that the suspect murdered the restaurant owner in the office, placed his body in the trunk of his car, and disposed of the body somewhere in the countryside. However, one might argue that you need a body and a weapon to conclusively prove that there was indeed a murder.

5. Answers will vary based on students' opinions and interpretations of the evidence as described in question 4. One could argue that murder convictions require a body, a weapon, opportunity, and motive. Although the suspect had motive and opportunity, there is no body or murder weapon to conclusively prove that the missing owner was actually murdered.